VOLUME
12

Originally published in the United Kingdom in weekly parts **COMBAT & SURVIVAL** is a study of the armed forces at work. It shows the skills taught to soldiers and the way in which military units operate. It examines the weapons and equipment used by different armies; and, by looking at recruit training and exercises, **COMBAT & SURVIVAL** demonstrates how the armed forces develop individual responsibility, leadership and initiative.

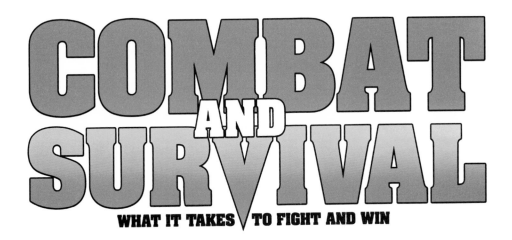

# COMBAT AND SURVIVAL

## WHAT IT TAKES TO FIGHT AND WIN

VOLUME
12

H. S. STUTTMAN, INC. *publishers*    Westport, Connecticut 06889

# Contents
## Volume 12

Published by H. S. STUTTMAN INC.
Westport, Connecticut 06889

© Aerospace Publishing 1991

ISBN 0-87475-560-3

# THE JUNGLE BATTLEFIELD

**Before attempting to operate in the jungle, you must understand the jungle environment. Common sense dictates how you function in a temperate climate, but special training and knowledge is required for jungle operations.**

The heavy rainfall and high temperatures encourage rapid and continuous growth of vegetation. Different types of jungle have evolved. Primary jungle is the original growth of tall, profusely leaved, evergreen trees which grow where the annual rainfall averages 200cms or more. These trees grow in three storeys: the first storey consists of trees some 10 metres high. This, combined with a second storey of trees up to 25 metres high, forms the thick canopy which blocks out the sun; the third storey, the tallest trees, can be as high as 60 metres.

A tangled growth of creepers hang from the trees, but the jungle floor is relatively clear. Fields of vision seldom exceed 50 metres, but you will find movement on foot is fairly easy as the trees are well spaced. The best going is always along crests or ridges.

Wherever primary jungle or deciduous forests are cleared and later abandoned, a secondary growth – known as 'secondary jungle' – results.

*US troops cross a river while on Search and Destroy operations against the Viet Cong. In some jungles, roads are few and far between and rivers are the main communication routes.*

*You don't have to be born in a rain forest to master the art of jungle warfare. These men are US Navy SEALs who often fought the Viet Cong on their own terms, on their own ground, and won.*

Exposure to sunlight causes bare areas to be rapidly overgrown by weeds, grasses, ferns, canes, and shrubs, which reach a height of two to three metres within a year. Secondary jungle also occurs on the edge of primary jungle, where light enters, resulting in a thin, but dense belt of undergrowth.

Tropical grassland is another feature of open country or high plateaux, where there is a long dry season. The grass can be up to five metres in height, is sharp-edged and extremely dense. Although movement through tropical grassland is difficult, it is immeasurably more so through secondary jungle, which is virtually impenetrable on foot. Visibility in both secondary jungle and grassland is down to a few metres.

## More sunlight

Deciduous forest occurs in areas which have a dry season lasting between three and six months. The trees are not as dense or as tall as in primary jungle, and some sunlight filters through the canopy, encouraging a more profuse undergrowth.

'Beach forest' describes the coastal vegetation found on dry ground at the rear of sandy beaches. It consists mainly of casuarina trees, which grow to a maximum height of 25 metres.

*Left: US Marines hump their way through heavy jungle in pursuit of their elusive enemy. The foliage cuts visibility to a few metres and reduces the burst radius of bombs and shells, but don't overestimate its value as cover.*

*Cadenas OP is a British post in Belize on the border with Guatemala. Movement on the ground is impossibly slow in the mountainous jungle, so all communications are by helicopter.*

*A pretty view of Belize, but a nightmare to have to traverse on foot. The helicopter is of enormous value in jungle operations both for mobility and pinpoint firepower.*

dom exceeds 15 metres.

Swamps are commonplace in tropical jungle, where there are wet, low-lying areas. Various palms thrive in swampy conditions, such as nipa and sago. Perhaps the most difficult form to negotiate is the mangrove swamp. These occur in coastal areas subject to tidal flooding: around river mouths, deltas and inlets, and along shallow bays or small islands and upstream as far as the tidal influence is felt. The mangrove's tangled roots are found above and below water level, making movement on foot very slow and difficult. Visibility is restricted to a few metres.

## Food plantations

Some areas of jungle are cultivated. This varies from primitive efforts of the more remote tribes, to the more-ordered, but still simple, agriculture of the bigger villages, to large-scale

Moss or mountain forest is found in some equatorial areas at high altitudes, usually but not always above 2,000 metres. The forest consists of a jungle storey of stunted, distorted trees, about six metres high. The tree trunks are covered in moss which is festooned from branch to branch, creating a dense canopy through which little light filters. The forest floor is often covered by a blanket of moss up to one metre thick. Movement on foot is slippery and slow, and the air is cold and still. Visibility sel-

# JUNGLE TACTICS

*The jungle environment dictates your tactics and weapons, taking over from the enemy as the dominant consideration. Troops must be trained to cope with the jungle first and foremost.*

**Health hazards**
These are endless: even a simple cut may become a serious problem. Life in the jungle is the ultimate challenge to personal administration as fungi, parasites and exotic diseases battle for parts of your anatomy.

**Weapons**
Most engagements fall into the bracket of close-quarter battle. You need something that is light, fast on target acquisition, controllable in recoil and preferably with a burst facility. Assault rifles like this M16A2 are ideal.

**Insects**
The insect life is as prolific as it is alien: some soldiers find this aspect of life in the jungle hard to handle. In some areas you have to clear a patch of ground with a machete just to be able to sit down. The mosquitoes can be so persistent that bites in the mouth can cause enough swelling to stop you being able to eat.

**Sniper shoot**
Locating the enemy is always a problem. The jungle makes the well-trained marksman an invisible enemy who can do you some real damage. In primary jungle, always keep a watch on the various tree levels as well as the ground.

**Air cover**
The jungle provides almost total cover from air recce, so large enemy concentrations can move undetected without the use of ground sensors and ground troops.

**Landing sites**
In some jungles the only way to get a helicopter on the ground is by hand cutting and explosives: there are occasions where a patrol in trouble may have to be winched out.

**Helicopters in the jungle**
The helicopter has revolutionised jungle warfare. In Vietnam it enabled very rapid insertion of troops into an area to complete a mission, their withdrawal with fire support or rapid redeployment to another area. This meant that fewer numbers of combat troops were required to dominate a particular area, so the ratio of combat troops to support troops was lower than in any previous conflict.

**Map coverage**
Map coverage is usually poor and the weather atrocious, which means your navigation skills have to be excellent. In some areas, if you get lost you will die.

**Humidity**
High humidity combined with sweltering heat means there is a definite limit to how much kit you can carry and still move: around 15 kg, depending on task and where you are. The kit you are carrying will literally rot off your back in days, not weeks.

**Engagement ranges**
You simply cannot see much further than about 30 metres at best in primary jungle. In secondary growth the wall of vegetation will cut this down to a couple of metres. In these conditions it is a question of who is the fastest gun in the West or East.

**Psychological effects**
Fighting in the jungle involves far more stress than other combat environments. Troops can only operate effectively in the jungle for relatively limited periods. The helicopter introduced the added shock factor of being taken from a Third World firefight straight to air conditioning, steaks and cold beer. This was a contributory factor to the heavy psychological casualty rates in Vietnam.

**Ground cover**
Ground cover varies with the type of jungle. The thick secondary growth or tropical grassland makes for very hard going, and it is difficult to move without making a great deal of noise. Moving tactically in this terrain, it may take an hour to cover 100 metres.

**Rivers**
The rivers are the roads of the jungle, and are the fastest routes, unless you have a helicopter. The rivers and canals of South Vietnam provided the infiltration routes from the Ho Chi Minh trail.

commercial plantations of coffee, rubber, tea, pepper, cocoa, coconut, oil palm, rice and other tropical crops. You will have to learn to operate in these plantations where terrorists may be seeking food and supplies.

In most equatorial jungle areas, the daily and seasonal mean temperatures remain constant throughout the year. Further away from the equator, these variations increase. Greater variations also occur at high altitudes, where it can be very cold at night, and in grassland, which traps the heat and can build up temperatures of over 37°C. In monsoon conditions and at night, humidity in the rain forest can rise to about 90°, which is near saturation. Annual rainfall is rarely less than 150 cms, and in some mountainous areas can be over 500 cms.

## Slowing things down

So what effect does the jungle have on your operations? It is not unfriendly or impenetrable to well-trained troops, but it does slow the operation down. Actions tend to be

# Combat Skills

Above: Casualty evacuation in the jungle is another vital role for the helicopter. Landing zones are carved out of the jungle with anything from chain-saws to special 15,000-lb bombs.

*In Operation 'Ranch Hand' the US Air Force sprayed 'Agent Orange' defoliant on the jungle to kill the vegetation that concealed Viet Cong positions and supply routes.*

*Above: A Navy PBR searches a sampan on the Perfume river. The Viet Cong regularly smuggled weapons and equipment past US patrols along river routes in Vietnam.*

isolated, and fighting often takes place at close range where a small force can influence a battle out of all proportion to its size. The thick vegetation means you come upon the enemy suddenly. This puts an unusually high mental strain on you and your men: it requires you to develop a sixth sense, to always remain alert, and to have reached a very high standard of weapon training and field craft. You have got to be quicker, better, fitter, more alert and more knowledgeable than the enemy.

## Difficult obstacles

The jungle canalises movement. The dense vegetation, deep eroded gullies, steep sided hills and ravines, the wide, swiftly flowing rivers create obstacles which make cross-country movement and resupply difficult.

Your progress through most secondary jungle can be painfully slow. Helicopters make a tremendous difference to mobility, but over-reliance on them means you are not playing the terrorist at his own game. You are not blending into the jungle, so you cannot surprise your opponent. By using helicopters you are announcing your presence.

The jungle reduces the effectiveness of modern firepower. The difficulty of observing and acquiring targets, means long-range weapons will be of limited use, but short-range weapons – particularly rocket and grenade launchers – will come into their own. Dense vegetation considerably reduces the effect of high explosive; the undergrowth and jungle canopy limit the bursting radius of bombs, artillery and mortar rounds.

## WEAPONS FOR JUNGLE WARFARE

*These SAS troopers are armed with SLRs, which are too long for jungle action and lack the capacity for automatic fire that is vital in anti-ambush action. Australians in Vietnam cut down some of their SLRs and altered them to fire full auto.*

*These Iban scouts in Borneo are armed with Browning A5 semi-automatic shotguns. With one of these you can get five rounds out in three seconds: bad news for the would-be ambushers.*

*Gurkhas in Sarawak in early 1966 are armed with an M16 and an L4 LMG. Light and handy, the M16 was soon popular with jungle fighting units. The L4 is lighter and more accurate than the GPMG but unable to provide the same weight of fire.*

## THE HOSTILE JUNGLE

Lack of water can be a severe problem: some parts of South East Asia have no rain for six months of the year. In addition to a heavy ammunition load you may need to carry up to 18kg (40lb) of water in the dry season. Although you may only cover a few kilometres a day when on patrol, you will need to be extremely fit to manage it successfully. Remember that one weak man can jeopardise the entire patrol.

*Left: A patrol which has run out of water and already has a casualty due to the heat looks up at the helicopter summoned to pick them up.*

*Below: The patrol stands in a clearing which is too small for the helicopter to land safely in. It is important for infantrymen to know how much space helicopters require!*

The velocity of a rifle round is also more quickly dissipated by the undergrowth.

But don't let the density of the vegetation deceive you into over-estimating the effectiveness of the cover from fire. The smaller trees may moderate the effect of enemy fire, but they will seldom provide adequate cover. At close range you must still maintain high standards of field craft, fire and manoeuvre.

### Health risks

Remember, the climate, the vegetation, the insect life and a number of endemic diseases all pose a considerable threat to your health and that of your soldiers. Not only are you more vulnerable to illness and disease in the jungle than in other climates, but it is very difficult to move a sick or wounded man to an area where he can be properly treated.

The main effect of the jungle on infantry is to slow the operation down, emphasising the importance of the individual soldier, and of operations at platoon and company level. At first the jungle is a frightening place, but, as you learn the rules of survival, as you begin to understand the vegetation, wildlife and climate, and as you become more expert in your jungle skills, you will grow in confidence.

*Fortunately this landing zone was nearby and the patrol was picked up successfully. It was not enemy action but lack of drinkable water that knocked them out. Jungle warfare requires high personal admin and survival skills.*

# Combat Report
## Vietnam:
## Engagement at Suoi Tre

Digging in the guns at a newly constructed firebase. The artillery was intended to support distant infantry patrols.

**Randall T. Elliott was a captain with the US 2nd Battalion, 12 Infantry, 25th Infantry Division, in Vietnam. In March 1967 his battalion met the Viet Cong at Suoi Tre near the Cambodian border.**

The US President, Lyndon Johnson, the man who once said Asian wars are for Asian boys, had decided to meet his military leaders at Wake Island – reflecting his growing concern for the way the war was going.

My story is similar to that of many other Americans engaged in the fighting end of the Asian war. Our patriotism, naivete and eagerness slowly gave way to nagging doubt, then fear – and the will to live. Many faced this well; others slowly slid into battle fatigue, and the line between that and insanity grew blurred.

## My fighting blood was up

We were in very dangerous territory. We had mounted a major operation called 'Junction City'. We saw the enemy often, and our patrols heard them a lot at night: signs that a fight was brewing. They were watching and following us closely, waiting for a mistake. They must have wondered what we were doing there: it was so near the Ho Chi Minh Trail that they could bring major units against us rapidly and with little warning.

We were staying in a fire-base with an artillery battalion. Another infantry battalion arrived, and the engineers constructed berms – walls – around the camp, making our awesome firepower even more effective. It limited Charlie's ability to see us and made his direct fire weapons less useful. Jesus, it was scary out there. Even though we were three battalions, we knew that there were at least three enemy regiments in the region, enough to wipe out an 800-man battalion in minutes.

About 9.30 in the morning on 21st March we came under the most intense mortar and rocket bombardment I had ever experienced. Five, six, seven hundred heavy explosions rocked through our positions. With this kind of firepower we knew that something big was up and that we were the target. Then it went quiet, and we knew Charlie was coming.

**Despite all the awesome firepower available, to the man in the foxhole a VC night attack was a hellish experience.**

You could see for almost a mile. The underbrush did not grow in this area, but there were a few tall mahogany trees. We rushed to the berms. It was already hot, and the air was filled with dust and the smell of cordite. In the distance we saw them forming up, row after row. Like the British at New Orleans. I could see their bayonets. My fighting blood was up, and I called to my men to fix bayonets. A cheer went up from 2,500 Americans. After long weeks, if not months, of hunting the elusive enemy, he was at last before us.

We wanted to go over that goddam berm and fight those people. Cooler heads prevailed, and we waited. My men began to straighten grenade pins, zip up flak jackets, check their ammunition and weapons. A few prayed; some ate and drank – maybe the last chance for a while. Others stared at the incredible sight unfolding in front of us.

The first assault elements were now a football field's length away, running towards us; some were firing and bullets were beginning to hit all around. Enemy sappers came into view, carrying engineer equipment to breech our berm. The commander of the laager ordered us to fire, and we did so before he'd even finished saying the word.

Our artillery pieces had been pulled up to the berm and were firing 'beehive' rounds as fast as they could. These were small steel darts that pinned enemy soldiers to trees and nailed their rifles to their chests. Machine-guns and assault rifles fired fully automatic, adding to the cacophony.

## We went over the top

The Viet Cong were coming from two sides. As they got closer, our men began to fall, and their mortar rounds were coming into our position. A bullet ripped through my fatigue jacket, just under my left arm. That was ****ing close. The VC were coming through, over the dead bodies of our men.

They committed their reserve force, and we felt the pressure. This time I wasn't sure our firepower would prevail. They were working around the other side of our position and we were taking casualties: about 75 men. We weren't yet desperate, but the going was getting harder.

Then, as suddenly as it began, and after several airstrikes, we sensed that they were about to quit. We couldn't hold back any longer, and with one loud scream and no-one in control we went over the top. I couldn't remember if my pistol was loaded or not, so I picked up one of theirs.

We attacked the few units and rearguard that remained. Gradually the smoke cleared and the firing stopped. We sent out a flying squad and they got the mortar crews and captured the mortars. The VC had been stupid to withdraw and not protect their guns.

The fight had lasted about 35 minutes. I began to count the bodies on the ground. I could see over 200 dead, including 27 Americans. The final count yielded over 1,000. I looked at them. Small, young and dead. They never had a chance; they could not fight us on our terms. But their leaders wanted to embarrass Johnson at Wake Island. So they came, wave after wave.

It was then I knew we would lose the war. Their political dedication was something we did not have. They would fight on empty stomachs with a few bullets against well-fed, superbly-equipped Americans. Somehow, it violated the sense of fair play I grew up with.

A few hours later, as I walked through the carnage, a Crane helicopter came in carrying a small bulldozer to dig a pit for the dead. I looked in the pit and saw row after row of mangled bodies. I couldn't help thinking, 'My god, are we Nazis?' I couldn't eat for a couple of days. A lot of generals came out and told us what a good job we did.

It was at Suoi Tre that I first began to shake all over. I don't know if it was the killing, the fear, or the knowledge that what we were doing might not be right. Now all I could do was hold on.

# OUTWITTING THE JUNGLE GUERRILLA

**If you are ever deployed in the jungle, study your enemy, his habits, his capabilities and his tactics. Because you fight at such close quarters in the jungle, everything happens much more quickly – if you have a thorough knowledge of enemy tactics you are much more likely to survive and win.**

The location of the world's jungles, and past experience, mean that your enemy will probably be an Asian, African or Latin American who is likely to draw his inspiration from extreme politics and his material aid from a neighbouring country. The individual guerrilla will probably be relatively uneducated, but deeply indoctrinated and fanatically dedicated to a cause; his leaders certainly will be. So the most likely threat is that presented by an enemy engaged in the type of operations most commonly described as revolutionary warfare, as first preached by Mao Tse Tung in China and since practised by the Viet Cong in Vietnam, the Chinese Communist Terrorists in Malaya and the Cuban Revolutionaries, and many others besides.

Revolutionary warfare can usually be divided into three phases. The initial phase is the subversive or passive phase, during which the revolutionary establishes his political base and strengthens his support amongst the population. It is a period of civil

*Armed with a Soviet RPD 7.62-mm LMG, a group of Viet Cong guerrillas prepare for action. In South Vietnam the guerrillas steadily progressed from minor raids to taking out whole battalions of government troops.*

*North Vietnamese troops attack, supported by rocket and artillery fire. Vietnamese communists defeated the French colonial army in the three stages of guerrilla war as described by Mao Tse Tung: subversion, insurrection, then conventional war. If you do not understand how guerrilla forces operate then you are doomed to repeat all the mistakes of the past.*

# REVOLUTIONARY JUSTICE

*The average man in the clearing is not interested in revolution. He is concerned with his family and the life of the village. But to win their revolution the guerrillas must have the villagers' support: they need food, recruits and revenue. In most cases the guerrillas use a 'carrot and stick' approach. Incentives to join the revolution may include murdering unpopular government officials, e.g. tax collectors and policemen. On the other hand, loyal citizens become the target of vicious terrorism.*

**Government by day/ guerrillas by night**
As the struggle in the villages intensifies the government often loses control of the countryside during the night. If you patrol through a village and find the people unco-operative, don't assume they are the enemy. They know that after you've gone the guerrillas will be back. This is why the British in Malaya moved whole villages to seal them off from guerrilla reprisals.

**The price of loyalty**
Guerrillas can destroy local government by killing officials or leading loyal citizens. Who's going to want to be the new teacher in Dak Son after the Viet Cong have murdered your three predecessors? One solution is to create a village militia led by a handful of Special Forces personnel who actually live in the village.

**Food supply**
Guerrillas need to eat too, and they will depend on the local population to provide their food. Find out what sort of food reserves a village would normally keep: an unusually large rice supply may indicate that the villagers are feeding the enemy.

unrest, disobedience and disturbance, when minor acts of terrorism against government officials and installations are likely to take place; it may last one or 20 years. Whether armed forces become involved at this stage depends on the strength and experience of the police force.

## Insurgency begins

The second phase is the active guerrilla insurgency phase. Large sections of the small rural population will by now be under revolutionary control. Each village will be likely to have its own small band of guerrillas, and each area a platoon or company of 'regular'

*Right: Khmer Rouge are seen on top of a bunker recently vacated by the Vietnamese Army after a fierce firefight.*

guerillas operating from the sanctuary of jungle bases.

Guerrilla attacks will be directed against the army, so you will certainly get involved. This second stage may last for years and, unless you are able to beat the guerrilla at his own game, the intensity and ferocity of guerrilla actions will increase, putting the army under mounting pressure.

The final phase is the counter-offensive, or final victory phase: the classic

**Firepower**
By tempting or tricking the government to use all the firepower at its disposal against a guerrilla position, the revolutionaries can often win the battle for village loyalty. If you call down an airstrike on a village to eject a force of guerrillas, the villagers are unlikely to be too impressed.

**Terminate with extreme prejudice**
This was the CIA jargon for killing supporters of the guerrillas in much the same way as the Viet Cong killed villagers loyal to the government. No arrest, no trial, just sudden death. Operation Phoenix inflicted mortal damage on the Viet Cong guerrilla movement and only conventional invasion by North Vietnam could achieve a Communist victory.

**ecruiting**
ter a long period of uerrilla war the villages are mptied of fit young men: ey are all in the overnment army or in the ush. The guerrillas will ometimes resort to onscription as well. During e Rhodesian war, large umbers of youths were hisked away to guerrilla aining camps over the order.

**Special Forces**
If you can beat the enemy at his own game by aggressive action with small patrols, you can do major damage to the guerrilla movement. Here part of a MAT (Military Assistance Team) arrives to deal with the local guerrilla problem.

example of a guerrilla campaign that was allowed to reach this phase was Vietnam. The guerrilla has by now become strong enough to engage the army in large and deliberate battles, using conventional warfare tactics.

## Guerrilla tactics

Guerrillas understand the advantages and limitations of the jungle, and have developed their tactics to make best use of the terrain. They will try to

**The Army and the People**
Guerrillas will try to divide the army from the population. Ambushes, booby-traps and sniping make the government troops cautious and suspicious of the locals, and the villagers soon resent the Army causing damage to their homes and animals. While it is difficult to think of war as 'state policy by other means' during a firefight, you must avoid the 'we had to destroy the village in order to save it' attitude of some US troops in Vietnam.

-FORSEY-

# B-40 ANTI-TANK ROCKET

The B-40 (also known as the RPG-2) is a Soviet anti-tank rocket now superseded by the RPG-7. Copied by the Chinese, it was widely used by the Viet Cong in both anti-tank and anti-personnel roles. Sometimes they would deliberately fire rockets high so that they detonated in the trees, causing a blast of shrapnel to catch APC or tank commanders with their hatches open. The RPG is also used in volleys, as the instant reaction to being ambushed.

dominate the jungle by forcing local inhabitants to help them. They will treat them ruthlessly, demanding food and punishing informers without mercy. Their base is likely to be located deep in almost inaccessible jungle, and their tactics will be aimed at preventing you from approaching these bases.

### Enemy harrassment

They will do this by harrassing you with small, mobile groups armed with rockets, rocket-propelled grenades and automatic weapons, and will induce you to pursue them with the object of luring you into an ambush. They will be expert at making a clean break from any engagement and melting into the jungle. They will often use small stay-behind parties of single machine-guns or snipers, possibly protected by mines or booby traps, which will force you to deploy and thereby to delay your advance and allow the main guerrilla body to escape.

### Concealed bases

Enemy jungle bases will be extremely difficult to pinpoint. They will be completely concealed from the air, and they will take full advantage of any natural obstacles such as rivers, swamps or precipitous approaches. Mines and booby traps will be liberally placed on all approaches, and bunkers will be strong enough to resist bombing and artillery fire. If the position is a large and permanent one, it will include extensive tunnel systems with vaults and rooms to allow the defenders to redeploy, resist attack or escape.

### Tactical withdrawal

Jungle guerrillas are not ashamed to withdraw to fight another day. They will use extensive delaying tactics, moving at night and scattering mines and booby traps, and laying carefully-prepared ambushes. Although they are likely to move mostly on foot, they may use boats on jungle rivers or requisition road transport to move large groups of men. In the later stages of revolutionary warfare they are likely to be able to use their own transport.

### Superior numbers

Jungle guerrillas will not, however, be limited to defensive operations and withdrawal. Whenever possible, and whenever they think they have superiority of numbers, they will quickly go over to the attack. Their attacks will be piecemeal, deliberate attacks with the aim of annihilating individual defensive positions.

### Well-prepared attacks

Never allow yourself to be put in such a situation. Once a guerrilla force has identified an enemy base that is cut off or vulnerable, or a garrison whose strength is depleted, it will strike. It will assault with successive

# JUNGLE EXPERIENCE

SAS in Borneo: here the guerrillas were mainly defeated by aggressive patrol action rather than massive conventional firepower.

The jungle campaigns fought since 1945 have all been conducted against a colonial background with a familiar administration and police system. Future operations are likely to occur in neutral or underdeveloped countries of which British forces may have no previous knowledge, and where local assistance may be limited. This makes it vital that you should understand the problems and demands of jungle warfare against a guerrilla enemy. Some of Mao's more illuminating principles of revolutionary war are:

**1** The campaign will last a long time
**2** Control of the population is far more important than taking and holding ground
**3** Initially outnumbered by the security forces, the guerrillas will mass to achieve local superiority for their attacks.
**4** Isolate the cities and people from their government

An Indonesian shot dead by British troops during the 'Confrontation'. Against jungle guerrillas, victory is judged by the bodycount.

*Above: Home-made terrorist sub-machine guns built from a rifle barrel and various bits and pieces. The lower one is based on the design of the Sterling SMG.*

*Below: Favourite guerrilla weapons cheerfully provided by the USSR – AKM assault rifle (top); SKS self-loading rifle; and PPSh sub-machine gun.*

*Bodies on the roadside in the wake of a vehicle ambush. Road-bound forces like the French in Indochina or British in Malaya in 1941 tend to lose jungle wars. You must learn to fight in the jungle with confidence.*

waves of infantry from different directions with intense fire support. Attacks of this type are usually well rehearsed and carefully prepared. Your defences may well have been tampered with, unknown to you: in Vietnam the Viet Cong were experts at creeping up to American positions and turning the Claymore mines around so that, when they were detonated, they scattered their deadly load in the direction of the defenders.

## Dedicated soldiers

Your enemies will be dedicated to their cause, they will have all the time in the world to achieve their aim, and they will be expert jungle fighters. The British Army has defeated successive opponents in the jungle – the Japanese in Burma, the Mau Mau in Kenya, the Chinese Communist Terrorists in Malaya, the Indonesians in Borneo and local insurgents in Brunei and Belize – and it has managed this by taking the guerrillas on at their own game and being better at it. In Malaya and Borneo, for instance, the British fought the enemy not with artillery and air power but by inserting small patrols armed in much the same way as the men they were seeking. The tactics that they used employed stealth, patience and cunning. This is the way to win in the jungle.

# Combat Report

## Namibia:
## Night Bush Patrol

**A Second Lieutenant in the South African Corps of Signals received his first posting to the operational area of South West Africa/Namibia in September 1980.**

This was my first experience of real soldiering. I fully expected to see terrorists behind every tree . . .

Two weeks after receiving my posting I was actually on patrol in the bush. The terrain in that part of SWA/Namibia is absolutely flat, with soft whitish sand that sharply reflects the light and makes walking a hard slog. The vegetation consists mainly of sparse grass, burned brown by the sun, and scrubby thorn bushes.

There is practically no surface water, and our ration of four litres per 48 hours in an average temperature of 38 degrees meant that every drop was precious. The flies, as always, were a nuisance, but what reduced us almost to screaming frustration were the Mopani Bees. These little demons, the size of small winged ants, hovered in a cloud right in front of us, and continually got stuck in the black camouflage cream that covered our faces and arms. Cigarette smoke and bad language failed utterly to discourage them, and swatting them with a bush hat gained only a few seconds' respite. Mopani Bees neither bite nor sting, but for pure infuriation and nuisance value I have never met the like.

Before starting out on our patrol we had undergone a week's revision of basic signalling skills applicable to the operational area, and had also revised the rudiments of infantry skills: section attacks, buddy aid, weapons handling, chopper drills, etc. I had enjoyed them immensely: section attacks with live ammunition were unheard-of at the School of Signals. As for having the opportunity to strip and fire the likes of the AK-47, the PKM and RPD machine-guns, and throw Russian and Chinese grenades . . . this was really it.

### A shape hurtled across the trail

I hadn't realised just how deeply this training had sunk in until the second day of the patrol. We were trudging through the bush, stoned on the heat and the monotony, trying to stay alert, when there was a sudden crashing in the bush a few yards ahead and to our right a shape hurtled across the trail to our immediate front. Even as I recognised it as a fox, I realised I was flat on the ground, rifle up and tracking the creature, and with my finger already taking first pressure on the trigger.

That night turned out to be memorable, not because of high drama but because of what, in a setting of unusual beauty, turned out to be high farce.

As dusk approached, we turned at right angles to our line of advance and then, after moving about a hundred metres into the bush, turned again at right angles to move back in the opposite direction from which we had come, and parallel to our original line of advance. After about another hundred metres, we stopped to eat. This act of dog-legging back to cover your own tracks while resting or eating means you are in a position to ambush anyone attempting to follow you.

### Misplaced ingenuity

You never set up your overnight TB (temporary base) in the same place as you halted to eat, but instead establish a new TB after dark to make things difficult for anyone trying to keep you under observation. I was explaining this to the corporal and two signalmen that were with me while we were finishing off our meal when I noticed one of the troops, Rocky, a know-it-all from Johannesburg where 'Daddy had pots of money', scooping bully from a ration tin – USING THE GAS PLUG FROM HIS FN/FAL RIFLE!

Fair enough, the fold-up rifle grenade sight that is part of the plug that holds in the gas piston and seals the gas chamber did, in fact, look rather spoon-like, but if you remove the gas plug your automatic rifle reverts to bolt-action operation.

### Radio silence

After a whispered apoplexy, we moved off and found a suitable spot for our TB without mishap. No digging in, as with only four of us it could only be a case of "shoot and scoot" if we were threatened. Anyway, sound carries distressingly far in the African night and even the muffled sound of entrenching tools in soft sand could advertise our position. Radio silence went without saying.

RHIP – Rank Hath Its Privileges. That meant I awarded myself the last watch, and rolled into my sleeping bag, boots, rifle and all, for six hours' kip before taking the last two-hour stag. Other privileges included lugging the HF, radio, maps and codes, spare radio battery, a belt for the machine-gun, and a full load of ammunition, rations and water.

I'd heard the old story of how the bushes moved when you were on stag at night, but this was my first experience of it. The area beyond our perimeter was a positive hive of activity – bushes moving around right, left and centre. At least I knew better than to trust my eyes; you rely on your hearing in the bush at night, as it is less likely to play tricks on you than your eyesight.

So, ignoring the bushes apparently in the process of stalking me, I started my stag sitting against a tree, rifle in my lap. A full moon and a cloudless sky gave our surroundings a silvery tint. The most spectacular array of stars, brighter than I've ever seen before or since, stretched across the deep blue-black of the sky. It was a sight that I could have stared at for hours.

### The rustling of a snake

It must have been towards the end of my watch, as the false dawn had already begun to show, that a rustling noise behind me caused me to sit up and look round. There, barely two metres away in the sparse, knee-high grass behind and to the right of where I'd been sitting, was what appeared to be a snake, slowly moving towards me. I catapulted to my feet, realising immediately that the worst thing I could possibly do would be to shoot at it – apart from giving the other members of the patrol the fright of their lives, I'd alert every terrorist within miles. However, the snake seemed to be moving in the direction of Pete's sleeping bag, so I lost no time in waking him.

The two of us crouched there, rifles at the ready, listening to the dry rustling sound that marked the snake's progress and seeing the silvery glint of its scales in the bright moonlight. The damn thing looked to be about as thick as my arm. I considered trying to bayonet it, but didn't fancy the idea of having to get that close. Pete wasn't much help; he just crouched there in silent amazement.

I was about to fix bayonets when I suddenly realised that, despite all the rustling and slithering, it didn't seem to have moved any nearer. Something was not quite right, and we cautiously moved in for a closer look, bayoneted rifles poised and our hearts hammering.

There was no snake: just the moonlight shining on the sand and grass. Our taut nerves and our imagination had supplied the rest. And the rustling? Simply a column of ants, almost invisible, but each one marching across the dead grass and dried leaves, and carrying a bit of grass in its jaws.

**A member of the South West Africa Territorial Force is evacuated after being injured by an anti-personnel mine. South African forces have developed a series of mine-proof vehicles, but there is no easy answer when you are patrolling on foot.**

# DOMINATING THE JUNGLE

**Above: A British soldier in Malaya fires his Bren gun, resting on the shoulders of his oppo. In this jungle campaign the British Army made extensive use of small patrols, playing the guerrillas at their own game.**

After Vietnam, the US Army has placed more emphasis on developing Special Forces units able to tackle a limited guerrilla war in, for example, Central America. Small teams of Special Forces leading locally recruited tribesmen were highly effective in some parts of Vietnam, and certainly more cost-effective than deploying divisions of regular troops.

*If you are going to defeat a guerrilla enemy, you will have to dominate the jungle: it is no good mounting operations from urban areas and then leaving the enemy to re-establish himself once you have gone.* You achieve domination of the jungle by establishing control of an ever-increasing area, within which you set up a network of bases and launch aggressive operations.

First of all, insert patrols into the area of jungle you have decided to dominate. These patrols will set up temporary patrol bases. The next stage is to locate and attack the enemy, using your patrol base. Once you have exerted a firm control over the area of jungle you are targeting, you can turn your temporary patrol bases into permanent bases occupied by a company or more.

## Divide the enemy

Repeat this cycle until separate controlled areas are linked and the enemy is prevented from operating effectively. As controlled areas are joined the enemy's lines of communication are cut, dividing his forces into isolated groups which you can destroy piecemeal. The greater the area over which you establish control, the more secure your permanent bases become. You can build up logistic support, and you can locate helicopters in most of the bases.

You must also control any settlements in or near the jungle. Ideally, this is a task for the local police, if they can be relied upon to do this job properly, but where there is no reliable civil or police organisation, control of the civil population must remain a military responsibility. The population must be prevented from supporting the enemy with supplies, shelter, recruits, labour and intelligence.

It is, though, your jungle bases that allow you to take on the guerrilla. The **patrol base** is the most basic of these: it is a place where a fighting patrol can halt for operational or administrative purposes for anything from two hours to several days. It may be the base

# SAPPER ATTACK

*Despite the awesome firepower at the disposal of the Americans, the Viet Cong frequently launched mass assaults on US Fire Support Bases in Vietnam. These FSBs were constructed within artillery range of one another to form a network of gun batteries which could then provide fire support for infantry patrols in the jungle.*

**Perimeter vigilance**
Don't think you are safe because you've wired the perimeter, sown a minefield and placed Claymores all around. The perimeter must be carefully observed, since NVA sappers were highly skilled at penetrating US defences and turning round the Claymores. Night vision kit is most valuable in this situation.

**Enemy bombardment**
Guerrilla heavy weapons tend to be limited to mortars, single 122-mm rockets and anti-tank weapons like the RPG-2 or RPG-7. However, in some cases you will still have to fortify your base to survive heavier bombardment. The North Vietnamese beat all their enemies with the help of powerful artillery and guerrilla armies often have a friendly power over the border who can supply fire support.

**Guerrilla planning**
The use of local people for such mundane tasks as washing can be a mistake. Many US bases were attacked by guerrillas who obviously knew their layout. A dawn sweep of the battlefield often revealed someone like the camp barber, dead on the wire with an AK in his hands.

**Punji stakes**
Sharp bamboo stakes can be driven into the ground around your perimeter to produce an effective barricade. They should be angled to impale an attacker at the waist.

**Suicide sapper**
Suicide sappers were employed against the French by the Viet Minh and regularly made their unnerving attacks on American units. Human bombs have been encountered more recently in the Lebanon. The only effective defence is accurate marksmanship, which can bring them down short of their target.

**Fire Support Base**
Surrounded by wire and mines and usually containing several infantry companies, FSBs were tough nuts to crack, but Viet Cong human wave attacks often penetrated the perimeter.

**Perimeter OP**
American FSBs often deployed observation posts outside the immediate perimeter to give warning of enemy presence. However, the guerrillas would often make a limited attack to catch anyone in a forward OP, making it a very dangerous job.

**Timing of the attack**
While their rockets and guns shelled the FSB, keeping the defenders' heads down, the NVA sappers crawled slowly forward. The moment the barrage lifted they could cover the last few metres a run and start flinging satchel charges over the wire.

from which your platoon is mounting an ambush, in which case you will probably occupy it for several days until the ambush is sprung or abandoned, or it may be a place where you stop for one night in the course of a long patrol.

## Jungle fort

The next level of base is the **forward operational base**. This is a permanent jungle 'fort' occupied by at least a company-sized unit. It will have an operations room controlling the area, a helicopter landing site, and mortars to provide fire support to patrols in the jungle.

These bases should be surrounded by wire entanglements and 'punjis' – sturdy fire-hardened bamboo sticks sharpened at both ends and driven into the ground at the appropriate angle to present an attacker with an array of needle-sharp bamboos at thigh height, upon which he will hopefully impale himself.

A trench and bunker system will allow you to man the perimeter in comparative safety. Clear the ground for up to 100 metres from the perimeter to create effective fields of fire. To complete a comprehensive defensive system, site Claymore mines to provide an electronically detonated explosive barrier around your fort.

Forward operational bases must be virtually impregnable to ground attack. They should be covered by a number of mutually supporting fire support bases, and the area around both forward operational bases and fire support bases must be patrolled constantly to deny its free use by the enemy.

The largest category of base is the **fire support base**. It will include artillery and mortars, which will provide fire support to the forward operational bases and patrols out in the jungle,

*A cache of North Vietnamese weapons captured in 1986 by Kampuchean guerrillas: 73-mm recoilless rifles, a 12.7-mm machine-gun, and a heap of AK-47s. Many guerrilla armies equip themselves with guns taken from their enemies.*

# Combat Skills

and will have to be manned by at least a company, or even a battalion. It will have a perimeter of mutually supporting bunkers and at least three strong points dominating the position, with overall control of the base being exercised from one of them.

All positions should be connected by tunnels or trenches. The perimeter should be strongly protected by a belt of mines, obstacles, booby traps, trip flares and command-detonated Claymore mines. In addition, you will need to establish warning devices and listening posts in the surrounding jungle to provide you with early warning.

Such a base will certainly require a helicopter landing site and perhaps an airstrip. If you do construct an airstrip, remember that it should be sited where it can be dominated by fire from the base, rather than expanding and weakening your perimeter to include it. In the midst of these defences you will need to construct water tanks, latrines and living accommodation dug in adjacent to your defensive positions.

## Patrol techniques

These jungle forts are not built to encourage a static defensive posture, but to serve as bases from which you can aggressively patrol into the jungle.

Reconnaissance, standing and fighting patrols are all used in the jungle. **Reconnaissance patrols**, consisting of up to eight men, are used to observe enemy or local habits and traffic, to collect topographical information on routes, obstacles and rivers, to select sites for bases, helicopter landing sites and ambushes, and to gather information on enemy bases.

Intelligence might indicate that the enemy has established a base in a particular area. Before committing a large force to attack it, you must pinpoint your target, evaluate its defences, decide on the best approaches, and calculate the exact size of the enemy force. In other forms of warfare, where you can see for greater distances,

# AUSTRALIAN SAS AND THEIR WEAPONS

The Australian SAS were among the most professional jungle fighters involved in the Vietnam War. Small patrols like this stalked the Viet Cong with an exotic collection of modified weapons and large quantities of Claymore mines. Unlike most American troops, the SAS used a lot of personal camouflage, including green mesh gloves and spray-painted guns and equipment. They won three Victoria Crosses in Vietnam, plus many other awards for gallantry.

**Right: A Sterling Mk 5, the silenced version of the Sterling SMG, with a 40-mm grenade-launcher fitted underneath. It fires 9-mm Parabellum with the muzzle velocity reduced to about 300 m/s.**

**An SLR heavily modified: the flash hider has been removed, the barrel cut down and the sear altered to allow fully automatic fire. New sights and a 30-round magazine complete the custom job, which results in a devastating short-range weapon.**

**Left: An Armalite AR-7 semi-automatic survival rifle chambered for .22LR rimfire with a silencer for subsonic shooting. The barrel and receiver can be dismantled and fitted into the stock and will float on water. Note the Silva compass on the soldier's wrist.**

*British troops use a tracker dog in Malaya to hunt down Communist terrorists. Aggressive patrolling can destroy the guerrillas' communications and force them onto the defensive.*

remote reconnaissance using various technical aids is usually possible, but in the jungle the only reliable form of reconnaissance is often a recce patrol using nothing more technical than the human eyeball.

**Standing patrols** will vary in strength depending on the task. Usually they are employed in the

*Patrol briefing: it is important to rehearse a patrol seriously, preferably with live ammunition. The success of a patrol is usually proportional to the planning and rehearsal beforehand.*

vicinity of a forward operational base or a fire support base to give warning of an enemy approach, but they can also be used to direct supporting fire or report on enemy or local activity in a given area. Here the dividing line between a standing patrol and a recce patrol is fairly thin. Essentially, a recce patrol will travel a relatively long distance to its target, whereas a standing patrol occupies a covert position much closer to your base.

**Fighting patrols** must be large enough and have sufficient firepower to destroy any group of guerrillas it is likely to meet. Their primary task is to deny the enemy freedom of movement or action in their area of re-

*Although rather discredited by the American experience in Vietnam, the bodycount is still an important gauge of progress against a guerrilla opponent. These bodies were recovered after a firefight in Malaya and await identification and burial.*

sponsibility by aggressive patrolling and ambushing. As a member of a fighting patrol it will be your job to harass the enemy, to follow him up relentlessly after making contact with him to attack his bases, and if possible to capture prisoners and dominate the area, destroying the enemy's morale.

## Victory in the jungle

The jungle guerrilla is an expert and brave opponent: it will never be easy to defeat him. The tactics that have been developed by the British Army in successive jungle campaigns are known to be effective. They rely on the steady expansion of small forces to the strength required to gain control of a zone of operations. Aggressive patrolling and ambushing from an expanding series of bases gradually puts the enemy on the defensive, strangles his control of the jungle, and puts his communications and logistic support at risk. The cycle is then developed until a complete region is brought under control and eventually the guerrilla army is defeated.

The disadvantage of these tactics is that they are extremely expensive in manpower. But although large numbers of troops are required to be successful, jungle warfare is still very much the province of the section and platoon commander. 'Small is beautiful' in the jungle. There is no room to deploy large formations, so, however large the total numbers of troops deployed in an area, they will consist of small patrols and ambushes fighting and working independently. In the jungle the individual counts.

# COOLING DOWN

**Below: Royal Marines approach the end of a run.**

**Your work-out does not end when you are exhausted; a cool-down, the third phase of your exercise period, is essential to restore your body to its resting states.** Studies suggest that people who are prone to heart disease suffer more heart attacks *after* exercise – because they didn't cool down properly – than during it. Keep moving, or you may become dizzy, light-headed or even lose consciousness.

**Stretching exercises prevent your muscles getting too stiff or sore. Your blood tends to pool in your legs during a comprehensive work-out; gentle cooling down exercises help redistribute it.**

## Advantages of a proper cool-down

### 1 Helping your heart

After exercise, veins carry blood back to your heart from areas where it has pooled (usually the legs). Gentle cooling-down exercises cause your muscles to squeeze the veins, which greatly assists the passage of blood back to the heart. Regular exercise is also essential in keeping your veins working properly.

### 2 Calming your mind and body

The cool-down helps to prevent stiffness and soreness – common in beginners – by removing the waste products and lactic acid from your worked muscles, and calms your body both physically and mentally by a gradual decrease in exercise intensity. Having relaxed muscles after a work-out is a wonderful feeling; the release of natural hormones (endorphines) from the brain leads to a pleasant state of euphoria that the non-exerciser will never experience.

# Suggested cool-down exercises

This is a good set of exercises to follow:

### 1 Brisk walking

Instead of sitting down, walk around briskly and bring your heart rate down to 100-120 beats per minute.

### 2 Deep breathing

Stand with your feet apart and hands on your hips. Breathe deeply: in through the nose and out through the mouth. Take 5-10 deep breaths, squeezing all the air out on each occasion, and relaxing your shoulders.

### 3 Arm circling

Stand with your feet apart and hands on your hips. Circle your arms backwards and together so that they come close to your ears.

### 4 Trunk bending and stretching

Stand with your feet wide apart and lower your trunk so that your hands touch the ground. Reach through your legs and then raise your arms above your head, breathing in on the way up and out on the way down.

### 5 Trunk bend and unroll

Stand with your feet wide apart and lower your arms and trunk to the ground. Unroll slowly to a count of 1-5 and finally breathe in deeply when standing upright. Repeat 5 times.

### 6 Arm and heel raise

Stand with your feet wide apart and your arms at your sides. Rise up on your toes and turn your palms outwards, taking a deep breath as you rise and breathing out on the way down.

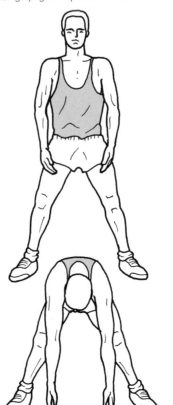

# Battle Fitness Programme No. 11
# TONING YOUR MUSCLES

**Without regular exercise you will develop a poor posture, over-use your joints and suffer from general weakness.** Your muscles need to regularly work at above 50 per cent of their maximum potential or they will become fatty and inefficient, but with proper muscle-toning exercises they will stay fit and healthy.

A muscle-toning exercise session can be carried out in a short period of time in the form of free-standing body exercises, free weights or using a well-equipped exercise facility.

## The benefits of muscle toning

### 1 Increased strength
As you become stronger you will be able to respond to physical challenges with confidence and increased satisfaction.

*By 'overloading' your muscles on a regular basis, starting with a gentle effort and progressively working harder, you will tone them up. They will not only feel healthier; they will look better and improve your whole body posture.*

**2 Leg presses**
It is essential to work on your leg muscles as all free weights are lifted with the legs, not your back.

**1 Bench press**
Breathe out as you push the weight up and out as you lower it gently back to your chest.

**4 Leg curl**
Now work your lower limbs. The leg curl exercises your hamstrings.

**3 Pull-down**
The pull-down exercises your back muscles in a safe and correct manner.

## 2 Ease of movement

If your body is fitter and stronger, your skeleton will be supported by well-conditioned muscles and you are less likely to be injured when your body is stressed.

## 3 Looking good

By regularly working your muscles you will develop and maintain good muscle tone and a lastingly athletic figure.

# The weight training programme

The most effective means of increasing muscle tone is to do weight training on a regular basis. Once you have learnt the basic principles and exercises, you will find that weight training can be a good release from the tension of daily life and immensely satisfying. The normal programme need only take about 30 minutes in a properly-equipped gym, and you should aim to work out two or three times a week.

You only really require eight main exercises in order to exercise your whole body effectively. If strength is your main requirement, you should use heavy weights but only a small number of repetitions. However, if you are aiming at increased muscular endurance then use lighter weights but repeat each movement more often.

## Eight main exercises

Most people are within reach of a gymnasium or weight room with instructors who can show you how to get the maximum benefit from the equipment. The following exercises are provided as a guide for a balanced programme, using equipment which is normally available in a fitness facility. The exercises follow a logical and physiologically sound order, working on the large muscle groups before the smaller ones.

1 **Bench press (chest exercise)**
2 **Leg press (leg exercise)**
3 **Pull down (back exercise)**
4 **Leg curl (hamstring exercise)**
5 **Shoulder press (shoulder exercise)**
6 **Arm curl (arm exercise)**
7 **Abdominal (stomach exercise)**
8 **Tricep press (back arm exercise)**

## Steps for a 10-week programme

1 Select exercises.
2 Determine the maximum weight that you can successfully repeat (One Repetition Maximum: 1RM) for each exercise.
3 Determine 60 per cent of the 1RM for each exercise. This will be your training weight.
4 Perform each exercise for 6-8 repetitions.
5 Do a set of exercises at least 3 times a week.
6 For Weeks 1 and 2 do two sets; from Week 3 onwards do three sets.
7 Re-test to measure your progress after 10 weeks.

**5 Shoulder press**
Push up against the weights to exercise your shoulders and arms.

**6 Arm curl**
You can use an arm curl machine instead of dumbbells to strengthen your biceps.

**7 Abdominal**
Use sit-ups to get used to the feeling of isolating your abdominal muscles before using abdominal machines.

**8 Tricep press**
Complete your work-out by exercising the muscles at the back of your upper arm, the triceps.

# Basic principles

There are four basic principles to weight training:

## 1 Overload

Regularly 'overloading' your muscles elicits a positive response; they thrive on physical work. 'Overloading' means exercising a muscular system against a resistance which is greater than normally encountered. You must work them at greater than 50 per cent capacity for the training to be effective.

## 2 Progression

For weight training to be of benefit you need to start slowly, gradually increasing the resistance over a given period of time. A muscle subjected to overload in a progressive manner will steadily increase its strength.

## 3 Specificity

Training is specific to the muscle group involved. There is no 'carry-over' effect, but you can tailor your exercises to suit individual needs, for instance for a particular sport.

## 4 Reversibility

All your hard work can be undone by prolonged periods of inactivity, so your programme must be continuous. This is why you have to do two or three sessions every week.

# STRETCHING TO DEVELOP AN AGILE BODY

*Your work-out is not complete without some simple stretching exercises. Besides being very relaxing, stretching helps enormously in preventing soreness and injuries.* A flexible body is essential for any active physical endeavour: skill is greatly enhanced if you can carry out a wide range of movements. Joints and muscles that are stretched regularly offer less resistance and require less energy for each movement to be carried out.

## Delaying the ageing process

As you get older, calcium deposits build up on the cartilage and surrounding tissues of your joints, which then become more difficult to move. People in sedentary jobs suffer even more as their bodies are not put through a full range of movement on a regular basis.

Inactive people also find that their muscles and connective tissue tend to shorten and their spinal column loses its elasticity, all this degeneration often leading to osteoarthritis. Regular stretching helps to delay this process.

### How to stretch

The stretching phase is normally done at the end of the work-out when the muscles are thoroughly warmed up; this makes the process more effective. Make sure that your range of stretching exercises includes each joint and muscle group.

**1** The ideal 'stretch and hold' period for each exercise is between 10-30 seconds.
**2** Enter each stretch in a slow, controlled manner without jerking or bouncing.
**3** Place the muscle in a position of maximum stretch. Breathe slowly and naturally to help relaxation.
**4** After a few seconds you will no longer feel the tension and the muscle can be stretched a little further. Stretch to the point where it feels good.
**5** Overstretching or holding for longer periods can cause pain, which is unnecessary.

*Regular stretching exercises extend your range of body movements and keep your muscles in good condition. It is particularly important to stretch your hamstring muscles to prevent tightness behind your knees after running.*

## Suggested exercises

Everyone has his own range of flexibility depending on his lifestyle and the amount of exercise he takes. So don't bother to compare yourself with others; unrealistic comparisons are de-motivating. Select from the following the exercises that will specifically help you.

### 1 Shoulder stretch

(a) Bring your elbow across your chest, pulling on the elbow with your opposite hand, and hold for 10-30 seconds.
(b) Using the same action, pull your elbow behind your head.
(c) Interlace your fingers behind your back and lift your arms up to the point of maximum stretch.

Do these exercises on both arms 2-3 times.

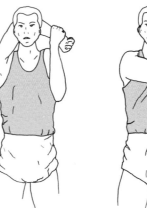

## 2 Chest raise

Lie face down with your arms bent and your hands flat on the ground under your shoulders. Gently raise your chest, keeping your pelvis on the ground, until your arms are straight. Repeat 5-10 times.

## 3 Cat stretch

Kneel with your arms outstreatched and tucked close to your ears, with hands extended. Gently lower your upper body and push down on your arms. Repeat 5-10 times.

## 4 Elongation stretch

Lie face down with your arms and legs extended. Elongate your body, stretching your fingers and toes, for a complete body stretch. Repeat 5-10 times.

## 5 Hip flexor stretch

Place your knee on the ground with one foot in front, with your hands rested on the forward knee. Push your hips down and then change legs. Repeat 5 times on each leg.

## 6 Single and both knees to chest

Lie on your back with your head rested, your back flat and legs extended. Grasping one leg, pull the knee into your chest and hold for 10-30 seconds. Do both knees alternately and then both together. Repeat 5-10 times.

## 7 Back rolling

Sit with your hands around your knees and then gently roll up and down on your spine. Repeat 5-10 times.

## 8 Spine twister

Sit upright and place one foot over the other extended leg. While supporting yourself with your hand, use your other arm to apply gentle pressure to the bent knee. Turn your trunk and look away as the action takes place. Repeat, using alternate legs, 5-10 times.

## 9 Sitting groin stretch

Sit upright with your knees apart and holding the soles of your feet flat together. Gently lean forward and lower your knees. Repeat 5-10 times.

## 10 Hamstring stretch

(a) Crouch with your hands flat on the ground and your knees inside your arms. Gently stretch your legs while trying to keep your hands on the floor. Repeat 5-10 times.
(b) Sit upright with one leg bent and your hands placed on your extended ankle. Gently bend your body forward from the hips. Stretch alternate legs 5-10 times.
(c) Sit upright with both legs outstretched and together. Bend gently forwards for 10-30 seconds. Repeat 5-10 times.

**Remember: By regularly stretching your body 2-3 times per week, you are making an important contribution towards peak fitness.**

## Stretching for runners

Regular stretching, especially of the hamstring tendon at the back of the knee, is particularly important for runners, who often experience tightness in the backs of their legs.

The hamstrings contract to prevent the forward leg being over-extended as the runner puts his foot down. This means the leg is never fully straightened during the running action, which causes tightness in the back of the knee and the lower back. In order to maintain a free and fluid range of motion it is therefore particularly important to stretch the hamstrings regularly.

# Firing the H&K Rifles

**'If it's good enough for the German army, it must be good enough for us,'** is the cry sounded by over 50 countries for the Heckler & Koch G3 rifle, and at the last count 14 countries were manufacturing it under licence. Add to that the G3SG/1, the PSG1, the HK33E, the G8 and the G41 and it becomes apparent that Heckler & Koch has a good design on its hands.

## War's end

A good design takes time to develop, and the history of the Heckler & Koch rifles goes back a long way. It began in 1945 when Mauser were developing a new rifle for the German army, but the war ended before they got beyond a prototype and the various engineers were scattered. Some of them arrived in Spain and began working for CETME, the Spanish weapons development agency; they took with them the drawings of the Mauser rifle and continued with the development until in 1956 they had a serviceable rifle.

## Inherited design

In an endeavour to sell it, the Spaniards gave a licence to NWM of Holland. And just at that time the newly-constituted Bundeswehr was looking for a rifle. It tested the NWM-CETME rifle, approved of some parts but disliked others, and gave the design to Heckler & Koch to improve.

Heckler & Koch was a post-war firm which, by coincidence, was at that time operating from one of the old Mauser factories, so that the rifle had come full circle and back to its birthplace. After three years of further development the rifle was adopted by the Bundeswehr as the Gewehr 3 (G3) in 7.62-mm calibre, and H&K then went to work to develop some variations.

The G3 is slightly unusual in using the delayed blowback system of operation, rarely seen in weapons firing such a powerful cartridge. The secret lies in the bolt; this is in two parts, a light front piece and a heavy rear unit, with two rollers lying between the two parts. As the bolt moves forward to chamber a round, the two

## The Heckler & Koch family

Left: Firing the HK33, which is a scaled down version of the G3, chambered for 5.56-mm ammunition. It has a more robust feel than an M16 but shooting characteristics are similar.

Right and above right: Loading the HK33's 25-round box magazine. The magazine is a sturdy piece of kit, unlike the tinny American M16 magazines currently being used with the British SA80 rifle. The G41 gives you an extra five rounds magazine capacity.

The cocking handle on Heckler & Koch rifles is on the left-hand side up near the muzzle. This is not as convenient as on the SLR or FN FAL.

Switching the safety catch down to 'E' (single shot). One stop further produces automatic fire on both the G3 and HK33. The G41 fires three-round bursts.

The sights give a 'V' rearsight for battle setting and apertures for 200, 300 and 400 metres. Zeroing for line and elevation is conducted on the rear sight.

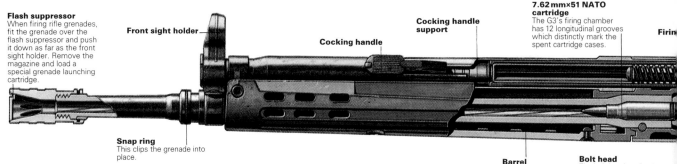

**Flash suppressor**
When firing rifle grenades, fit the flash suppressor and push it down as far as the front sight holder. Remove the magazine and load a special grenade launching cartridge.

**Front sight holder**

**Cocking handle**

**Cocking handle support**

**7.62 mm×51 NATO cartridge**
The G3's firing chamber has 12 longitudinal grooves which distinctly mark the spent cartridge cases.

**Firin**

**Snap ring**
This clips the grenade into place.

**Barrel**

**Bolt head**
The bolt head carries two rollers which project into recesses in the barrel extension. These retard the rearward movement of the bolt head, so that this moves at a quarter of the speed of the bolt carrier.

**Follower and spring**

**Magazine**
The G3 uses a 20-round magazine like the SLR, but the heavy-barrelled G8 can be belt fed or use a 50-round drum.

# Inside the Heckler & Koch G3

The G3 was the great rival of the FN FAL in the 7.62-mm market during the 1960s, and it was adopted all over the world. By offering a scaled-down version able to fire 5.56-mm ammunition, H & K are cashing in on the excellent reputation of the G3, which has proved to be a rugged and accurate rifle.

*The G41 has been developed specifically for the 5.56-mm NATO round and follows NATO specifications throughout. It includes a bolt-closing device, a bolt catch to hold the bolt open after the magazine has been emptied, and takes NATO standard 30-round magazines. It is built to sustain a service life of 20,000 rounds and, as seen here, can be fitted with a bipod. This is the Italian version, built under licence by Franchi to enter in the Italian army competition.*

halves of the bolt are kept apart by the rollers, which ride on the interior of the gun body.

As the cartridge is chambered, the front half of the bolt is stopped; but the rear half is still moving, driven by a spring. The front end of this half is sloped, so that as it moves forward it can force the rollers outwards and into recesses machined in the side of the gun body. Everything now stops moving and the rifle is ready to fire.

## Firing process

Pulling the trigger releases a hammer and drives a firing pin forward to fire the cartridge. The explosion pressure pushes the cartridge backwards, and it pushes on the front half of the bolt. This cannot move back because the two rollers, lodged in the walls, prevent it moving, and the rollers cannot move because the front part of the rear half of the bolt is still in place, forcing them outward.

# Stripping the G3

**1** Check that the chamber is empty and remove the magazine.

**2** Depress the pin that holds the butt and receiver together.

**3** Remove the pin from the other side of the weapon: make sure that the bolt is closed when you do this.

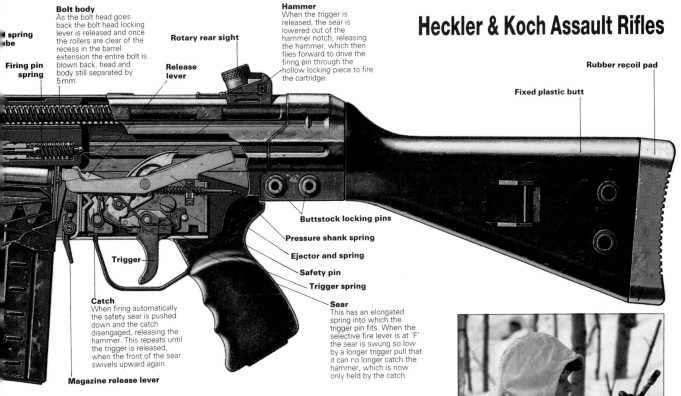

**Bolt body**
As the bolt head goes back the bolt head locking lever is released and once the rollers are clear of the recess in the barrel extension the entire bolt is blown back, head and body still separated by 5 mm.

**spring tube**

**Firing pin spring**

**Rotary rear sight**

**Release lever**

**Hammer**
When the trigger is released, the sear is lowered out of the hammer notch, releasing the hammer, which then flies forward to drive the firing pin through the hollow locking piece to fire the cartridge.

# Heckler & Koch Assault Rifles

**Rubber recoil pad**

**Fixed plastic butt**

**Buttstock locking pins**

**Pressure shank spring**

**Ejector and spring**

**Safety pin**

**Trigger spring**

**Trigger**

**Catch**
When firing automatically the safety sear is pushed down and the catch disengaged, releasing the hammer. This repeats until the trigger is released, when the front of the sear swivels upward again.

**Sear**
This has an elongated spring into which the trigger pin fits. When the selective fire lever is at 'F' the sear is swung so low by a longer trigger pull that it can no longer catch the hammer, which is now only held by the catch.

**Magazine release lever**

But the recesses in which the rollers lie have been very carefully designed so that under pressure the rollers can roll back and be squeezed inwards; as they do so, they squeeze the shaped front end of the bolt's rear half and begin to force it back as well. Slowly, the whole bolt begins to move, all at different speeds, until the rollers gradually squeeze the rear part of the bolt backwards sufficiently to allow them to roll clear of the recesses. And as soon as they do that, everything clicks into place. The bolt becomes a one-piece assembly once more, and is driven smartly back against its spring, extracting the spent case and cocking the hammer. When it runs back the whole cycle begins again.

The first thing to come from the G3 was the G3SG/1, since the German army wanted a sniping rifle. This is no more than a G3 which has, during its factory testing, shown itself to be particularly accurate.

## Police use

A step up from the G3SG/1 is the PSG/1; this is the same action mechanism but allied to a heavy barrel and a very sensitive trigger.

The last of the 7.62-mm members of the family is the G8 rifle, previously called the HK11E. This has been specially designed for use by police and anti-terrorist forces.

When the 5.56-mm cartridge began to make its presence felt in the 1960s, H&K soon developed a suitable rifle, simply a scaled-down G3 using exactly the same system of delayed blowback. This has gone through several minor changes and is now known as the HK33 rifle.

When NATO adopted the 5.56-mm cartridge as standard, it did so with a

*This Norwegian soldier is on exercise with British forces in northern Norway. Norway is one of 14 countries to manufacture the G3 rifle under licence.*

**4** The top receiver now comes away from the lower receiver.

**5** Pull the bolt assembly out of the upper receiver.

**6** Here the two-part bolt is removed from the weapon, ready for cleaning.

new and heavier bullet than the American M193. This meant that weapons like the HK33, which were rifled to suit the M193, did not perform well enough with the new cartridge. H&K has therefore developed the G41, rifled to suit the NATO bullet and generally the same as the HK33 but having the addition of a three-round burst mechanism.

It would be unfair to leave H&K without mentioning its revolutionary

*The HK33 stripped down. Designed around the M193 cartridge used by the M16, the HK33 does not perform so well with the new NATO standard 5.56-mm cartridge based on the SS109 bullet.*

# Battlefield Evaluation: comparing

## Heckler & Koch assault rifles

Nobody can compete with Heckler & Koch for the diversity of a single family of rifles; the weapons included in this comparison are H & K's main rivals for military orders. The highly successful G3 captured a large part of the market for 7.62-mm assault rifles and, with the G41, H & K have produced a first-class weapon designed to fulfil all NATO standard requirements. Meanwhile, H & K's revolutionary G11 is waiting in the wings.

**Specification:** (G3)
**Cartridge:** 7.62-mm NATO
**Weight:** 5.15 kg
**Length:** 1025mm
**Cyclic rate of fire:** 550-600 rounds per minute
**Magazine:** 30-round aluminium or steel box

**Assessment**
Reliability      ★★★★
Accuracy      ★★★★
Age      ★★★★★
Worldwide users   ★★★★

*The heavy-barrelled G8 rifle is specially designed for police and paramilitary use.*

## FN FAL

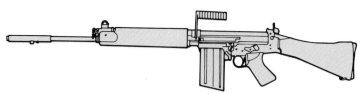

This was the G3's most obvious rival; those armies that wanted a 7.62-mm rifle and did not buy the G3 usually took the FN FAL. There is little to choose between them for accuracy and reliability, and it really comes down to which of the two you feel happier with.

**Specification:**
**Cartridge:** 7.62-mm NATO
**Weight:** 5 kg
**Length:** 1143mm
**Cyclic rate of fire:** 650-700 rounds per minute
**Magazine:** 30-round magazine

**Assessment**
Reliability      ★★★★★
Accuracy      ★★★★
Age      ★★★★★
Worldwide users   ★★★★

*Firing the Self-Loading Rifle on exercise, fitted with a Blank Firing Attachment (BFA).*

## Steyr AUG

Since this weapon has recently been adopted by Australia and New Zealand as well as by Morocco, Austria and Oman it is a very strong contender even though its appearance upsets some people. Clad in plastic with a transparent magazine and a built-in optical sight, this bullpup model is arguably the best 5.56-mm rifle in the world.

**Specification:**
**Cartridge:** 5.56-mm × 45
**Weight:** 4.1 kg
**Length:** 790mm
**Cyclic rate of fire:** 650 rounds per minute
**Magazine:** 30- or 42-round transparent plastic box

**Assessment**
Reliability      ★★★★
Accuracy      ★★★★
Age      ★
Worldwide users   ★★★

*The Steyr AUG is winning more export orders by the day; Oman is the latest country to adopt it.*

G11 rifle. This is totally different to any other H&K rifle, or any other rifle anywhere for that matter since it is 4.7-mm calibre and fires a caseless cartridge. This has been under development for several years and is planned to go into service with the Bundeswehr in 1990.

### G11 caseless rifle

A remarkable weapon, it can fire single shots, automatic, or three-round bursts at the phenomenal rate of 2,300 round per minute – in effect, one pull of the trigger produces a prolonged roar and three shots have gone before you feel the recoil. But that's another story.

*Portuguese paratroopers patrol the streets of Lisbon, armed with G3 rifles made in Portugal, during Left Wing demonstrations in the early 1970s. Portuguese troops used G3s in the colonial wars in Angola and Mozambique.*

# the H&K assault rifles with rivals

## IMI Galil assault rifle

The Galil comes closest to the Heckler & Koch 'family' concept since the same design is available in 7.62-mm and 5.56-mm versions and there is also a very well made sniper model. There is no doubt about its combat capabilities since both Israel and South Africa have used it 'for real' without complaint. Based on the Kalashnikov, the Galil in either calibre is an excellent weapon.

**Specification:**
(5.56-mm rifle)
**Cartridge:** 5.56-mm × 45
**Weight:** 5.2 kg
**Length:** 979 mm
**Cyclic rate of fire:** 650 rounds per minute
**Magazine:** 35- or 50-round magazine

**Assessment**
Reliability     ★★★★
Accuracy     ★★★★
Age     ★★★
Worldwide users  ★★★

*The Galil is one of the few rifles to have been scaled down like the H & K series. This is the 7.62-mm ARM.*

## Beretta AR 70/90

This 5.56-mm design is still undergoing trials by the Italian army, but once these are completed it will be a formidable contender in the international market. Extremely well made, highly accurate and giving single shots, automatic or three-round bursts, this new Beretta has some innovative features.

**Specification:**
**Cartridge:** 5.56-mm×45
**Weight:** 3.99 kg
**Length:** 986 mm
**Cyclic rate of fire:** not disclosed
**Magazine:** 30-round box

**Assessment**
Reliability     ★★★★
Accuracy     ★★★★
Age     ★
Worldwide users  ★

*The SC 70/90 is Beretta's entry to the Italian army competition: yet another first-class weapon from Beretta.*

## FN-FNC 5.56-mm rifle

This is FN's 5.56-mm rifle, which has so far been adopted by Belgium and Sweden. A locked breech weapon using a rotating bolt, again there is little to choose between this and the Heckler & Koch G41 for serviceability and accuracy. Many prefer the G41 because it seems to sit better in the hand.

**Specification:**
**Cartridge:** 5.56-mm NATO
**Weight:** 4.36 kg
**Length:** 997 mm
**Cyclic rate of fire:** 600-700 rounds per minute
**Magazine:** 30-round box

**Assessment**
Reliability     ★★★★
Accuracy     ★★★★
Age     ★★
Worldwide users  ★★

*Fabrique National's entry to the 5.56-mm market, the FNC, is a sound and reliable rifle.*

# Tracked Firepower:
# Soviet self-propelled artillery

*East German 152-mm self-propelling guns trundle past an admiring crowd at a recent parade. The new series of Warsaw Pact SP guns is undermining NATO's superiority in mobile artillery, and gives Soviet tank divisions much greater tactical flexibility.*

*Joseph Stalin referred to artillery as 'the God of War', a description which reflected the Russian army's historical enthusiasm for massed batteries of heavy guns as well as the Soviet tactics then being developed on the Eastern Front. During World War II the Soviets used artillery on a greater scale than any other army, employing several thousand guns at a time to subject German positions to a fearsome barrage that pulverised the enemy's front line.*

With their belief in the primacy of nuclear weapons, the Soviets allowed their artillery to stagnate during the late 1950s and early 1960s. Hub-to-hub batteries of World War II era guns continued to be employed, while NATO forces adopted flexible tactics based around a series of self-propelled guns such as the British 105-mm Abbot and the American M109 155-mm and M110 203-mm weapons.

The need for a new generation of weapons and a tactical re-think became apparent to the Soviets during the 1960s, and the capability of their artillery has steadily increased ever since.

## The devolution of self-propulsion

Soviet ground forces received several excellent towed artillery pieces in the 1960s, notably the D-30 122-mm 'Sonyushka', which first appeared in 1963. Although by the standards of towed artillery the D-30 was light and versatile, it was still vulnerable to counter-battery fire and totally unprotected in an NBC (Nuclear, Biological and Chemical) environment.

*Soviet 122-mm self-propelled guns cross a pontoon bridge on exercise. This light gun is called the 'Gvozdika', which means 'carnation'!*

*The 2S1 122-mm gun provides close fire support for Soviet tank units, deluging enemy anti-tank gunners with HE while the T-72s make their attack. In the last stage of the assault, the SP guns will follow up the second wave of BMP Infantry Fighting Vehicles.*

*The 152-mm self-propelled gun fires a mixture of ammunition including 2-kt nuclear shells. Note the gunner's large periscope in front of the commander's cupola.*

The need for a protected self-propelled vehicle with a fully traversible gun mounted on the chassis rear was agreed, and instructions given to GRAU (gun development) and the Central Auto-Tractor Directorate (Ts Au Tu) to co-ordinate the fusion of such tried-and-tested guns as the D-30 and 152-mm D-20 with the new generation of chassis then being fitted to the new generation of tracked vehicles.

## Successful pieces

Two excellent artillery pieces, the 152-mm 2S3 'Akatsuja' and the 122-mm 2S1 'Gvozdika', resulted. Both are now in service throughout the Warsaw Pact and form the cornerstone of divisional and regimental artillery.

The 'Akatsuja', known originally as M-1973 after the year of its introduction, is clearly intended to rival the United States' M109 155-mm howitzer. It is in essence an old D-20 barrel fitted with a modified breech and new fume extractor, fitted into a large new turret mounted onto the rear of a virtually unchanged SA-4 'Ganef' chassis.

The 152-mm gun/howitzer fires a High Explosive Fragmentation Projectile weighing 43.6 kg to a maximum range of 17,300 metres. A new rocket-assisted projectile (RAP) with a staggering range of 37,000 metres has reportedly been developed.

## Weak protection

In conjunction with most Soviet field artillery, the 'Akatsuja' has a direct-fire capability utilising an APHE (Armour Piercing High Explosive) projectile capable of piercing 127 mm of armour at a range of 1,000 metres. Although this 48.8-kg projec-

tile would prove devastating against enemy APCs, using the gun in an anti-armour role would be a hazardous business as the 'Akatsuja's' own armour protection is very weak.

A maximum of 40 rounds are carried, of which at least 35 are usually high explosive, and are fed into the vehicle through two small rear ports feeding into a conveyor belt. Power-assisted loading gives a rate of fire of approximately three rounds per minute, or a sustained rate of fire of up to 60 rounds per hour with a well trained crew. 'Akatsuja' is capable of firing 2-kiloton nuclear missiles: a point hopefully not lost on those presently discussing nuclear arms reduction.

The ungainly turret, far larger than that fitted to the United States' M109, is fully NBC proofed, fitted with a full range of night driving equipment and provides plenty of room for the commander, loader and gunner to operate. The driver sits forward in the chassis to the left of the main gun, with the commander directly behind him in the main turret. A 7.62-mm machine-gun, mounted on the forward part of the commander's cupola, provides the only close-quarter defence.

The other two members of the six-man crew do not travel in the gun itself, but with the ammunition resupply vehicle close behind. They have the unenvable task of operating in the open, totally unprotected from shrapnel or NBC attack, and must long for promotion to a safer, if more complex, position inside the vehicle itself.

### 122-mm 2S1 'Gvozdika'

The 'Gvozdika', known originally as the M-1974 after the year of its introduction, has no direct NATO equivalent. It was designed specifically to give localised support to tank and BMP-1-equipped motor rifle regiments, each of which is equipped with a battalion of three six-gun batteries for its independent use.

The deceptively bulky hull, developed from that of the MT-LB artillery tractor, provides enough buoyancy to allow the 2S1 to float with little preparation. Prior to entering the water a small track cover, normally stowed on the rear of the turret, is placed over the front of the hull to direct the water flow over the tracks, which provide the only form of propulsion when in the water. A set of swim vanes is attached behind the tracks and a cover placed over the engine air intakes to prevent flooding. Early suggestions that the gun can be fired when swimming have since been discounted.

The main armament, with its elevation of +70°, depression of −3° and turret traverse of 360°, consists of a modified version of the 25-year-old D-30 122-mm towed howitzer fitted with a double baffle muzzle brake, fume extractor and modernised breech block. A high explosive projectile weighing 21.8 kg with a muzzle velocity of 690 metres per second can be fired to a maximum range of 15,000 metres.

A fin-stabilised HEAT (High Explosive Anti-Tank) projectile weighing 14.1 kg may be fired in the direct fire role to penetrate 460 mm of vertical armour at a range of 1,000 metres, but this is once again defensive rather than offensive, as at that distance the gun would be well within the effective range of any of the latest generation of NATO APCs.

# Inside the Gvozdika

Each Soviet tank division is supported by 72 of these self-propelled 122-mm guns, which have the military designation SO-122 and the industrial number 2S1. By attaching groups of these guns to relatively small tactical units, the Soviets have sharply increased the ability of their tank and motor rifle formations to punch a hole through NATO defences.

Forty rounds of mixed ammunition, mainly high explosive, are carried and can be fired at a burst rate of five rounds per minute, although sustained fire is considerably slower. When the gun is in a sustained fire mode the normal four-man crew is supplemented by two additional loaders to ensure a steady supply of ammunition, but bearing in mind that the internal loader is working under extremely cramped conditions and that each round weighs 14.1 kg it is easy to see why rapid fire cannot be maintained for very long.

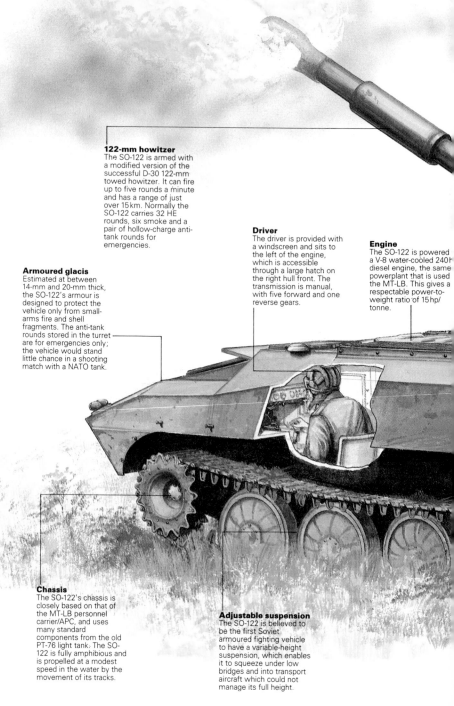

**122-mm howitzer**
The SO-122 is armed with a modified version of the successful D-30 122-mm towed howitzer. It can fire up to five rounds a minute and has a range of just over 15 km. Normally the SO-122 carries 32 HE rounds, six smoke and a pair of hollow-charge anti-tank rounds for emergencies.

**Driver**
The driver is provided with a windscreen and sits to the left of the engine, which is accessible through a large hatch on the right hull front. The transmission is manual, with five forward and one reverse gears.

**Engine**
The SO-122 is powered a V-8 water-cooled 240 h diesel engine, the same powerplant that is used the MT-LB. This gives a respectable power-to-weight ratio of 15 hp/ tonne.

**Armoured glacis**
Estimated at between 14-mm and 20-mm thick, the SO-122's armour is designed to protect the vehicle only from small-arms fire and shell fragments. The anti-tank rounds stored in the turret are for emergencies only; the vehicle would stand little chance in a shooting match with a NATO tank.

**Chassis**
The SO-122's chassis is closely based on that of the MT-LB personnel carrier/APC, and uses many standard components from the old PT-76 light tank. The SO-122 is fully amphibious and is propelled at a modest speed in the water by the movement of its tracks.

**Adjustable suspension**
The SO-122 is believed to be the first Soviet armoured fighting vehicle to have a variable-height suspension, which enables it to squeeze under low bridges and into transport aircraft which could not manage its full height.

# Soviet Tracked Firepower

## Developments

The Soviets are clearly very satisfied with their early experiments with self-propelled artillery; so much so that they have now introduced a new generation of larger guns. A long-barrelled 152-mm gun, mounted on the same chassis as the 2S3 but without the armoured turret protection, has now entered service and has a giant 203-mm gun with an estimated range of over 30,000 metres. Airborne troops now have their own dedicated self-propelled howitzer and new vehicles can be expected to enter service in the near future.

Tracked artillery is far more expensive than towed guns, both in terms of actual cost and man-hours spent in maintenance. The Soviet Union,

**Gunner**
The gunner uses the periscope forward of the commander's cupola to sight the gun for indirect fire. There is a sight for direct fire mounted to the right of the main armament. The gun is loaded by a fourth crew member seated to the right of the gun and he throws the empty shell cases out of his hatch.

*The 152-mm SP gun, military designation SO-152, may have an automatic loader as it has two hatches in the turret rear that look like reloading hatches for an automatic magazine. Its gun has a range of 18,500 metres and is believed to carry 46 rounds of ammunition.*

**Commander**
The commander directs the operation of the vehicle in accordance with orders received from the CO of the artillery unit. The Soviet command system distributes SO-122s at battalion level, but this artillery will only support the unit to which it is attached. It is a rigid and potentially wasteful system.

**NBC system**
An air filter is fitted in the back of the turret, and the SO-122 has an overpressure system to keep out nuclear or chemical contamination.

**Tracks**
The SO-122 normally travels on 400-mm tracks, but when operating in snow or over swampy areas it is fitted with special tracks 670mm wide, which reduce its ground pressure.

The SO-152 operates in battalions of 18 vehicles, which are attached to Soviet tank and motor rifle divisions as well as serving in independent artillery brigades. Their mobility makes them difficult to locate and destroy.

unlike NATO, seems to regard this as a good investment, having revolutionised her artillery assets at all levels during the last decade.

### Limited improvements

Although NATO was the first to introduce self-propelled artillery, until recently she did little to modernise her assets and even now is limiting her improvements to the up-barrelling of such existing assets as the M109 and M110.

An attempt was made to fit the British/German/Italian FH70 155-mm gun onto a Leopard MBT chassis, but, after years of national infighting, frustration and failure, the new weapon

# Battlefield Evaluation: comparing

## 2S3 'Akatsiya'

The 2S3 'Akatsiya' (Acacia) entered service with the Soviet army in the early 1970s, 10 years after NATO armies adopted the similar M109 self-propelled gun Each Motor Rifle or Tank division has 18 of these vehicles; their 152mm guns can reach out to 18km and can fire conventional explosive, chemical or anti-tank ammunition. A 2-kiloton tactical nuclear shell is also available.

**Specification:**
**Crew:** 6
**Combat weight:** 23 tonnes
**Road speed:** 55km/h
**Power to weight ratio:** unknown
**Length:** 7.1m
**Height:** 2.7m
**Armament:** 1×152-mm gun; 1×7.62-mm machine-gun

**Assessment**
Firepower          ★★★★
Range              ★★★
Age                ★★
Worldwide users    ★★

*Introduced 20 years after their NATO equivalents, the new Soviet SP guns were long overdue.*

## GCT 155-mm gun

Based on a lightened AMX-30 chassis, the French GCT was accepted by the French army in 1979 and is proving highly successful. An automatic loader enables the crew to be reduced to four and helps the gun come into action in under two minutes. In tests it has fired over 100 rounds an hour, and a burst facility allows a rapid salvo of six rounds in 45 seconds, useful in a mobile battle in which the gun must move quickly to avoid enemy counter-battery fire.

**Specification:**
**Crew:** 4
**Combat weight:** 42 tonnes
**Road speed:** 60km/h
**Power to weight ratio:** 17hp/tonne
**Length:** 6.7m
**Height:** 3.25m
**Armament:** 1×155-mm gun; 1×7.62-mm machine-gun

**Assessment**
Firepower          ★★★★
Range              ★★★★
Age                ★★
Worldwide users    ★★

*The French GCT 155-mm gun has an automatic loading system with an impressive rate of fire.*

## M109 155-mm gun

The M109 is one of the most widely used self-propelled guns in the free world. First introduced into the US Army in 1963, it has needed several modernization programmes to maintain its effectiveness but up-dated fire control systems and improved ammunition make it a very capable weapon. The latest model, the M109A5 has loader assist devices to increase the rate of fire, better armour protection and an effective NBC system.

**Specification:**
(M109A2)
**Crew:** 6
**Combat weight:** 25 tonnes
**Road speed:** 56km/h
**Power to weight ratio:** 16hp/tonne
**Length:** 6.1m
**Height:** 2.8m
**Armament:** 1×155-mm howitzer; 1×7.62-mm or 12.7-machine-gun

**Assessment**
Firepower          ★★★★
Range              ★★★
Age                ★★★★★
Worldwide users    ★★★★★

*The M109 set the pattern which the Soviets have belatedly imitated with their 152-mm self-propelled gun.*

system, initially designated SP70 but later more realistically labelled SP90, was scrapped at huge financial cost.

The Soviet Union now has the 2S1 and 2S3 artillery at regimental and divisional level as good as any in the world. The 2S1 can advance anywhere in support of the tanks and mechanised infantry, while the 2S3 can give withering fire support wherever needed. Both have been exported throughout the Warsaw Pact and the 2S3 is now playing an important role in the Iraqi army in its war against Iran. Both of these excellent weapons are certain to remain in widespread service for many years to come.

*The SO-122 self-propelled gun has no direct NATO equivalent except perhaps for the British Abbot. Its most important role is to provide quick-response indirect fire ahead of advancing Soviet tanks. If this is to be successful the Soviets will have to improve their battlefield communications.*

# the 2S3 with its rivals

## M110 203-mm gun

The heaviest Western SP gun, the M110 is operated by a 13-man crew, five riding on the vehicle and the rest in an M548 tracked cargo carrier which carries the ammunition. The gunners are completely exposed to the elements and enemy fire and the vehicle is not amphibious. Its rate of fire is about one round every two minutes, the ammunition is separate and the various rounds all weigh over 90 kg. Chemical and nuclear shells are available.

**Specification:**
(M110A2)
**Crew:** 5 (on vehicle)
**Combat weight:** 28 tonnes
**Road speed:** 54 km/h
**Power to weight ratio:** 14 hp/tonne
**Length:** 5.7 m
**Height:** 2.9 m
**Armament:** 1×203-mm gun

**Assessment**
Firepower ★★★★★
Range ★★★★
Age ★★★★
Worldwide users ★★★

*The monstrous M110 has provided mobile heavy artillery support to NATO forces in Germany.*

## Abbot 105-mm gun

The British Abbot is a lightweight gun by modern standards and was to have been replaced by the SP70, a joint British/German/Italian development which came to nothing. The ammunition is the same as the towed 105-mm light gun and a very rapid rate of fire can be maintained for short periods, up to 12 rounds per minute. Six HESH anti-tank rounds are carried in case the enemy front line turns out to be closer than anticipated.

**Specification:**
**Crew:** 4
**Combat weight:** 16.5 tonnes
**Road speed:** 47 km/h
**Power to weight ratio:** 14.5 hp/tonne
**Length:** 5.7 m
**Height:** 2.5 m
**Armament:** 1×105-mm gun; 1×7.62-mm machine-gun

**Assessment**
Firepower ★★
Range ★★★
Age ★★★★
Worldwide users ★★

*The Abbot, supposed to be replaced by the now abandoned SP-70, still equips close support regiments of BAOR.*

## M107 175-mm gun

The M107 shares the same chassis as the M110 and complemented the heavier 203-mm gun by having a longer range. The US Army has since abandoned the M107, up-gunning its M107s to M110 standard, and other NATO users may follow suit. The US Army used the M107 in Vietnam, its long range allowing firebases to be built quite far apart. Israel still uses the M107 and has tested a new round which can reach out to 40 km, ideal for shelling Arab anti-aircraft positions in advance of an IDF airstrike.

**Specification:**
**Crew:** 5 (on vehicle)
**Combat weight:** 28 tonnes
**Road speed:** 56 km/h
**Power to weight ratio:** 14.3 hp/tonne
**Length:** 5.7 m
**Height:** 3.6 m
**Armament:** 1×175-mm gun

**Assessment**
Firepower ★★★★★
Range ★★★★★
Age ★★★★
Worldwide users ★★★

*US Army M107s have now all been upgraded to M110 standard, but Israel and the UK continue to use it.*

# Bush Fighting
## with the Ratel

**The Ratel is designed for operations in the South African bush; this demands very long range and great mechanical reliability. Combat experience in South West Africa and Angola has led to a number of improvements on the original design.**

**The Ratel is tough — it has to be. The terrain it operates in is some of the most hostile in the world, which alone inflicts harsh punishment, to say nothing of the guerrillas against which it is deployed.** The Ratel infantry combat vehicle is named after a species of South African honey badger. Despite its small size, the original Ratel is a fierce creature that is not only capable of absorbing a great deal of physical damage but is an implacable and aggressive fighter. The Ratel vehicle is thus well named, for it too is a formidable opponent.

## Tough conditions

The first Ratel was built in 1974 and was designed from the start to be used under South African conditions. This means long missions over rugged and variable terrain where it can expect little maintenance. It also has to be well armed and able to carry all its own supplies, spares and a good-sized complement of men.

Over the years the Ratel has met all these demands and there are now several versions of the basic vehicle, all of them using the same basic 6×6 drive and armoured hull. The power-pack is a six-cylinder diesel engine located at the left rear. It provides the power needed to drive the Ratel over all manner of harsh terrain and the punch to push the vehicle through dense bush, including young trees.

## All-terrain vehicle

The Ratel is a true all-terrain vehicle. It rarely has to cross water obstacles under South African conditions, but if it does it can ford up to 1.2 metres. From his central position well forward in the hull the driver has excellent vision through three large bullet-proof windscreens. These are covered by armoured shields if there is any serious shooting in progress, and he then uses periscopes. The gear box is automatic and the vehicle is very easy to drive.

The driver has his own roof hatch

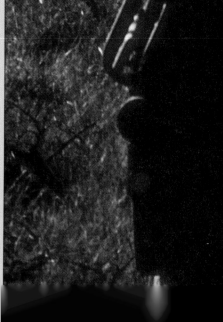

**A convoy of Ratels 'on externals', i.e. engaged in operations across the border with Angola. With no action imminent the troops stay on top of the hull where it is cooler and where they are less likely to be injured if their vehicle hits a mine.**

but he can enter and leave his position from within the vehicle, so if he is wounded he can be replaced without anyone having to leave the shelter of the armoured hull. The hull is designed to be proof against the effects of land mines: any that go off under the hull will just blow off wheels and will only rarely penetrate the shaped armour, which has been specially designed to withstand blasts from most anti-tank mines.

If a Ratel is damaged on operations it is never left behind for an enemy to loot. Every Ratel can be fitted with a small crane jib or tow bar at the rear, and these are used to tow damaged vehicles out of action.

## Hydraulic doors

The hull has entry doors at the left and rear, operated by hydraulics to ensure they open and close at all vehicle angles. There are also many roof hatches, often left open most of the time until the shooting starts. A Ratel can carry up to 11 fully-armed and

*A Ratel 90 Infantry Fighting Vehicle fires one of its 81-mm smoke dischargers, which can be detonated by either the commander or the gunner.*

equipped troops, including the driver.

For a vehicle of its type the Ratel is very well armed. The basic vehicle, the Ratel 20, has a two-man turret mounting a 20-mm cannon and a 7.62-mm MG4 co-axial machine-gun, the South African version of the old 0.30-in Browning M1919. Over a hatch at the rear there is another MG4, used for local and air defence, while some vehicles also carry an extra MG4 over the turret. The occupants can fire their R4 rifles through the four firing and vision ports provided along each side. South African soldiers frequently supplement their armament with captured RPG-7 rocket launchers, and the Ratel is roomy enough to accommodate them.

### Fire support vehicle

There are many different Ratels – the Ratel 90 is a fire support vehicle with a 90-mm turret gun, and the Ratel 60 turret carries a short breech-loading mortar, again for fire support, but it is also a powerful anti-ambush weapon that can fire a canister round to produce a fan of steel balls over a wide area at short ranges.

There is a command version of the Ratel with a 12.7-mm Browning heavy machine-gun in the turret and a Ratel mortar carrier with a 81-mm mortar firing through the roof hatches. It is anticipated that a version carrying some form of anti-armour guided missile will be seen in the near future.

All these various forms of Ratel operate over very long ranges, often deep into neighbouring states around the borders of South Africa to knock out terrorist strongholds and bases; the most frequent targets are SWAPO bases in Angola.

During such operations, the Ratels are loaded with all manner of equipment and supplies. Spare wheels are carried lashed to the hull roof, food is

# Inside the Ratel

Powered by a turbocharged, six-cylinder direct injection diesel developing 282 hp, the Ratel is exceptionally agile, and since its combat debut in the 1982 invasion of Angola has proved to be a rugged and reliable APC. It is superior to the Soviet-supplied APCs and armoured cars such as the BTR-60s and BRDMs used by Angola, and can take on anything short of a Main Battle Tank.

**Firing ports**
The Ratel has three bullet-proof vision blocks with a firing port underneath on each side.

**Rear machine-gun mount**
Two hatches open on the right rear of the roof and there is a circular mount with a hatch cover below a mounting for a 7.62-mm machine-gun.

**Rear door**
On the right-hand side of the hull rear is a door, the lower part of which folds down to make a step.

**Internal kit**
The Ratel carries a formidable amount of kit inside: tow bar and cables, petrol stoves, two 50-litre water tanks, radios, intercom and handset, plus 1000 metres of cable and a full set of picks and shovels.

**Infantry section**
The infantry in the troop compartment sit on bench seats down the centreline of the vehicle. The Ratel 20 has a total crew of 11, but the Ratel 90 carries 10 as its 40 rounds of 90-mm shell take up a great deal of space.

*Ratels are shown being serviced after returning from an operation. Ratel columns perform a great deal of maintenance in the field, and their already cramped interiors are further crowded by the addition of spare parts and enough supplies for several weeks' action.*

stacked wherever there is space, and there always seems to be room for a few cases of beer. The usual number of 7.62-mm machine-gun rounds carried is at least 6,000. Spare whip aerials for the radio are always carried somewhere on the hull, as these break continually when Ratels shove their way through dense bush.

### Equipment fit

Two drinking water tanks are fitted as standard, and each vehicle carries cooking stoves, a comprehensive tool kit, a tow bar and cables, and spare parts. At least one vehicle in every four-Ratel troop tries to carry a field shower outfit. The overall emphasis is on self-sufficiency from fire support to first aid, for out in the border country there are no nearby bases and no supply dumps, other than those which can be captured.

**81-mm smoke dischargers**
These can be fired by either the gunner or commander and quickly provide a dense smokescreen to conceal the Ratel from the enemy.

**Commander**
The commander sits on the left of the turret with the gunner on the right. The commander's cupola has vision blocks for all-round observation while closed down.

**Two-man turret**
Ratels are fitted with the same turret as carried on the Eland armoured cars used by the South African Army. This example is fitted with a 20-mm cannon and co-axial machine-gun, but the FSV 90 carries a 90-mm semi-automatic gun firing HEAT rounds to an effective range of 1200 metres.

**20-mm F2 cannon**
Turret traverse and weapon elevation are manual on the Ratel 20; the cannon can elevate to +38° and depress to −8°. It fires High Explosive rounds to an effective range of 2000 metres and armour-piercing ammunition to 1000 metres.

**Roof hatches**
There are four roof hatches above the troop compartment which are hinged on the outside and can be locked open to provide welcome ventilation.

**Driver's station**
The driver has excellent visibility through three big bullet-proof windows. In action, these are covered by steel shutters at the touch of a single lever within the vehicle. The driver's station is connected to the rest of the vehicle so you can change drivers without anyone having to get out.

**All-welded steel hull**
The Ratel's side armour is 8-10mm thick, proof against small-arms fire up to 7.62-mm calibre and shell splinters. The frontal armour is 20-mm thick and will keep out 12.7-mm machine-gun rounds, but the 14.5-mm and 23-mm anti-aircraft weapons sometimes encountered defending guerrilla camps can destroy a Ratel.

*Below: Smoke break for the commander and gunner of a Ratel 20 leading a column of Buffel mine-resistant personnel carriers.*

The self-sufficiency is carried to the point of changing engine packs in the field. Each Ratel column is usually followed by a convoy of trucks, some of which carry repair crews who can replace a Ratel engine pack in about 30 minutes. The convoy also carries fuel and ammunition and some other supplies, but in the main each Ratel has to carry its own needs for sometimes well over two weeks.

### Cramped interior

Consequently Ratel interiors are crowded and cramped while on operations, and it comes as no surprise that the roof hatches are kept open as long as possible with the crew spending most of their time sitting on the roof or with their heads out of the hatches.

In action, Ratel crews can either fight their way through an objective by firing their weapons through the weapon ports as they drive through, using the turret guns to add their firepower, or they can dismount for action, in which case the turret guns are used as mobile fire support.

### Effective firepower

The 20-mm cannon and 90-mm guns carried by most Ratels have a useful anti-armour capability and can knock out most of the lightly-armoured vehicles or strongpoints that they are likely to encounter, and they are also very effective anti-personnel weapons. The Ratel 60s and mortar-carriers tend to stand back during the final stages of attack operations to supply indirect fire support, but they too can use their weapon ports to provide more firepower.

Most Ratel operations are fairly

20-mm cannon shells are quite a handful: the Ratel's cannon is capable of knocking out any of the Soviet APCs supplied to Angola or Mozambique.

simple in military terms. Columns up to a battalion strong leave their base somewhere near a border and make deep incursions into neighbouring territory. The exact positions and nature of the terrorist bases involved are already well known from the efforts of recce teams who have scouted the locations and approach routes for weeks in advance.

### Native scouts

These teams often operate on foot and usually involve local natives who know the country well. Using their guidance the column makes its approach at speed and across country to avoid land mines on the roads and tracks. As it gets nearer the objective, most moves are made by night.

### Guns blazing

The final approach is made under cover of darkness with the attack commencing at dawn by all available vehicles charging forward in line abreast with all guns blazing. The actual fire fights usually last only minutes, with the guerrillas fading into the local country to hide and come back another day – they are short of anti-tank weapons and can do little against the well-armed Ratels and their well-trained crews.

Not all Ratel work is of such a dramatic nature. Many Ratels are used for

# Battlefield Evaluation: comparing

## Ratel IFV

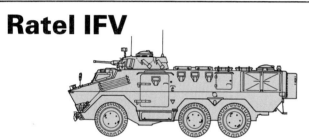

Designed from the start to operate under South African conditions, the Ratel is an extremely tough and well-armed vehicle. It has a good range, can carry a wide range of supplies, and is well armoured. It has cost the South Africans a great deal to design and produce but will last in service for years. Some sales have been made to Morocco and production has now ceased.

**Specification:**
**Combat weight:** 18.5 tonnes
**Maximum road speed:** 105 km/h
**Power-to-weight ratio:** 15.24 hp/tonne
**Length:** 7.212 m
**Height:** 2.915 m
**Crew:** 3+8
**Armament:** cannon or gun; machine-guns; mortar; port rifles

**Assessment**
| | |
|---|---|
| Firepower | ★★★★★ |
| Protection | ★★★★★ |
| Age | ★★★ |
| Worldwide users | ★★ |

*Ratel production is now complete, and the South African Army has a large fleet of tough and reliable APCs.*

## Light Armored Vehicle

Originally a Canadian vehicle derived from the Swiss MOWAG Piranha, the 8×8 LAV is now in production for the US Marine Corps in several versions, including 25-mm cannon-armed vehicles, recovery vehicles, cargo carriers, mortar and guided missile carriers and command vehicles. Other variants are planned. Protection is generally light to keep down weight and increase mobility.

**Specification:**
**Combat weight:** 12.88 tonnes
**Maximum road speed:** 100 km/h
**Power-to-weight ratio:** 23.4 hp/tonne
**Length:** 6.393 m
**Height:** 2.69 m
**Crew:** 3+6
**Armament:** cannon; machine-gun; TOW missiles

**Assessment**
| | |
|---|---|
| Firepower | ★★★★ |
| Protection | ★★ |
| Age | ★ |
| Worldwide users | ★ |

*The Swiss MOWAG series of vehicles are also tough customers; the US Marines have adopted a modified Piranha*

## EE-11 Urutu APC

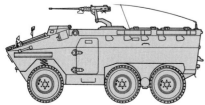

The Brazilian EE-11 Urutu has done much to make Brazil a major arms exporting nation, and is a 6×6 vehicle with numerous configurations. It has been sold widely and is in use with Iraq in the Gulf war. Simple, with few technical frills but amphibious, it is relatively cheap to produce and purchase.

**Specification:**
**Combat weight:** 14 tonnes
**Maximum road speed:** 105 km/h
**Power-to-weight ratio:** 18.6 hp/tonne
**Length:** 6.1 m
**Height:** 2.72 m
**Crew:** up to 13
**Armament:** gun or cannon; machine-guns

**Assessment**
| | |
|---|---|
| Firepower | ★★★ |
| Protection | ★★ |
| Age | ★★★★ |
| Worldwide users | ★★★★★ |

*Brazil has established itself as a major arms exporter. The EE-11 is cheap, simple and reliable.*

little else than escorting convoys and border patrolling to keep an eye on the vast tracts of open country that guerrillas could use to infiltrate peaceful areas. During these patrols each Ratel has an operational range of around 1,000 km, so they rarely need refuelling as would similar vehicles.

### Robust vehicle

One thing marks the Ratel above all others – its extreme toughness. It can operate under conditions that would wreck many similar vehicles, and it can travel great distances without breaking down. Yet when the Ratel enters a fight it can hold its own against any comers.

*South West African Territorial Force troopers rush to man their Ratel APCs against SWAPO guerrillas crossing into the country from Angola.*

# the Ratel with its rivals

## VAB APC

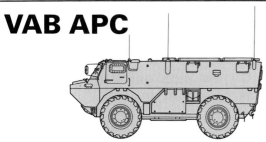

The French VAB (Véhicule de l'Avant Blindé) has been in production since 1973 in both 4×4 and 6×6 forms and in a wide range of weapon fits. It has been adapted to suit many different combat roles from mortar carrier to riot control vehicle, and has been produced as a guided missile launcher. It has been sold widely, mainly to ex-French colonies.

**Specification:**
**Combat weight:** 14.2 tonnes
**Maximum road speed:** 1 km/h
**Power-to-weight ratio:** 15.5 hp/tonne
**Length:** 5.98 m
**Height:** 2.06 m
**Crew:** 2+10
**Armament:** gun or cannon; machine-guns; guided missiles; mortar

**Assessment**
| | |
|---|---|
| Firepower | ★★★★ |
| Protection | ★★ |
| Age | ★★★★★ |
| Worldwide users | ★★★★★ |

*The versatile VAB is one of the most widely exported wheeled APCs and serves in a variety of combat roles.*

## BMR-600 IFV

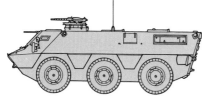

The Spanish BMR-600 underwent a lengthy development process but is now in production in amphibious and non-amphibious forms. It is relatively lightly armed and usually has no turret, although some development models have tested a 90-mm gun and guided missile launchers. Some have been sold to Egypt and Saudi Arabia.

**Specification:**
**Combat weight:** 13.75 tonnes
**Maximum road speed:** 100 km/h
**Power-to-weight ratio:** 23 hp/tonne
**Length:** 6.15 m
**Height:** 2 m
**Crew:** 2+11
**Armament:** machine-gun and mortar

**Assessment**
| | |
|---|---|
| Firepower | ★ |
| Protection | ★★ |
| Age | ★★★★ |
| Worldwide users | ★★★ |

*The BMR-600 is manufactured by the Spanish company, Pegaso, and has won a number of export contracts.*

## BTR-60P APC

One of the most widely used of all Soviet APCs, the 8×8 BTR-60P has been in large-scale use since the early 1960s. It can be found with or without overhead armour and some models have a small turret while others are used as radio carriers. It is a simple and basic vehicle with only light protection and medium mobility and has now been supplemented by the later BTR-70.

**Specification:**
**Combat weight:** 9.98 tonnes
**Maximum road speed:** 80 km/h
**Power-to-weight ratio:** 18 hp/tonne
**Length:** 7.56 m
**Height:** 2.055 m
**Crew:** 2+ up to 16
**Armament:** machine-gun

**Assessment**
| | |
|---|---|
| Firepower | ★ |
| Protection | ★ |
| Age | ★★★★★ |
| Worldwide users | ★★★★★ |

*The BTR-60 is now showing its age but its reputation as a rugged and reliable vehicle still remains.*

# Snakes, Crocs and other Varmints

**When you're living off the land, you have to be on the lookout for anything and everything that's edible. That means being prepared to catch and eat some pretty unfamiliar dishes — anything, from an insect to a reptile.** Better a venomous snake for supper than slow starvation. Snakes and lizards, in fact, are delicious, and there are some restaurants in the world that charge high prices for snake meat. In this section of the survival course you can learn how to trap and cook lizards, snakes, turtles, frogs, newts and salamanders – not to mention crocodiles.

### Take care

All snakes found on land or in fresh water are edible, whether they are poisonous or not. If you don't know if the snake you're hunting is poisonous, assume it is and act accordingly. Take extreme care when approaching the snake, and use a long stick or a hefty stone to kill it.

### Kill the snake

You can, if you prefer, pin it to the ground by the head before killing it. Pick up the snake from behind. Put your index finger on the top of its head, and your thumb and middle finger on each side, just behind the

*Frogs usually make good eating, but not these. Their skin contains one of the world's most deadly poisons. Central American Indians roast the beasts on sticks and scrape the resulting toxin onto their hunting arrows. One millionth of an ounce of the poison will kill a 6-kg monkey. Generally, avoid all brightly-coloured small animals.*

jaws. You must keep your index finger on top of the head to stop the reptile turning inside its skin and biting you.

Next, chop the snake's head off, making the cut a couple of inches behind the head itself. But don't relax your guard. Even after you've cut it off, its reflexes may still be active

*This anaconda snake is just about to squeeze the life out of an interfering human. Constrictor snakes such as these (some grow up to 12 metres long) live in jungles around the world and wait in low-lying tree branches before dropping onto hapless victims who wander underneath.*

*Tree-dwelling green mambas are from a group that kills more people than any other. Three drops of their venom will kill you, and as they only deliver a small proportion of their venom each time, they can go on to kill a few of your mates as well. And they can move at up to 5 mph.*

enough to make the severed head bite you. Be careful!

### Snakebite

Snakes kill their prey in one of two ways: constrictors squeeze it to death, the rest bite. Not all snakebites are poisonous, and very few poisonous

*Cobras generally live in tropical scrub farmland and often make their homes under peasant huts, so be careful where you bed down for the night. Though they usually rear up and bite their victims, some species spit their venom up to 2 metres, aiming for the eyes. The poison can be absorbed into the bloodstream through the eyes, and you can be dead inside the hour.*

# Preparing a snake for eating

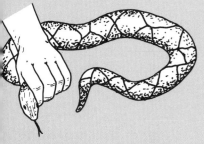

**1** Hold the snake firmly behind the head.

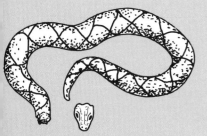

**2** Cut the head off with a knife.

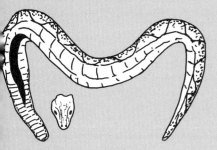

**3** Slit open its belly and remove its innards. Use these to bait snares and traps.

**4** Skin the snake. You can use the skin for improvised belts, straps or similar items.

*Snakes are good to eat and, according to this Japanese soldier, this is the best way to skin them. Before trying it yourself, make certain that you've cut the head off with at least 5 cm of body. Otherwise you'll get a mouthful of venom!*

bites will kill you if you treat them promptly enough.

Walking around, the place you're most likely to get bitten is on the lower leg, well away from the heart. Unless the snake manages to hit a vein by chance, you have time to act before the poison can spread into the bloodstream. These are the signs of a venomous snakebite:

**1** Between one and four puncture marks at the site of the wound
**2** Local pain
**3** Local swelling within the first two hours after the attack
**4** Paralysis, twitching, numbness and general weakness within two hours

Remember, the poison has to spread in the bloodstream before it can do serious, lasting harm. If you panic or get excited, your pulse will speed up, and that will cause the poison to spread faster. Stay calm.

You don't need to be quite so careful with lizards: there are only two poisonous species in the world, the

# First aid for snakebites

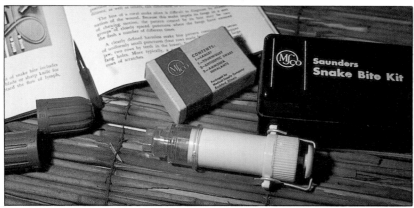

*In a snake kit the lancet is used to open the wound so the blood carries the poison out of the body. Tourniquets restrict the circulation and limit the spread of the poison. In an emergency a bit of broken glass and some rope will do the job.*

All snakebites should be treated as poisonous, and first aid must be given at once. The US Marine Corps manual recommends that you carry out the following while waiting for evacuation to the nearest hospital or aid station.

**1** Kill the snake if possible. If you can identify it, this may help in deciding on the treatment. Call for medical evacuation immediately.
**2** Keep the victim quiet and calm. Keep the bitten part still and below the level of the heart.
**3** Place a constricting band between the bite and the heart. Tighten the band just enough to produce slight bulging of the surface veins. Make sure that circulation has not been stopped.
**4** If swelling develops above the constricting band, remove the band and apply it above the swelling.

## Nerve poison
For neuro-toxic (nerve poison) snake bites, such as cobra, coral snake or sea snake, medical evacuation and immediate administration of anti-venom is essential but you may have to act quickly in the meantime.

**1** The venom will attack the nervous system and the victim may stop breathing. If he does, apply artificial respiration.

**2** If heartbeat and breathing stop, apply CPR (cardiac pulmonary resuscitation).
**3** Do not suck the wound; you may ingest the poison.

## Blood poison
For haemo-toxic (blood poison) snake bites, such as rattlesnake, copperhead and viper, take the following action if the victim cannot be at a hospital within an hour of the bite.

**1** Make a cut over each fang mark, parallel to the bitten limb. The cuts should be no more than half an inch long and a quarter of an inch wide.
**2** Apply suction to the wound. If a snakebite kit is available, use its suction pump. If not, suck by mouth, spitting out the blood and other fluids frequently. Haemo-toxic venom is not harmful in the mouth unless there are cuts or sores and even then there is not much risk. Suction should be kept up for at least 15 minutes before loosening the tourniquet.

**ALL SNAKEBITE VICTIMS SHOULD BE TAKEN TO HOSPITAL.** The Mojave green rattlesnake has a slow-working haemotoxin; the snake can bite you and you'll feel fine, but 10 hours later you'll be dead.

*The Puff Adder is one of the largest of the viper family and lives in the drier parts of the East African bush. Thick and heavy snakes, they like to enter camps in the bush, so watch out for them, especially in piles of logs. Their poison is not very strong but they give you a very large dose of it.*

Gila Monster and the Beaded Lizard. They are both found in the Americas, roughly between Panama and the south-western United States. Club them, or catch them in a running noose on the end of a long stick.

Skin and clean snake before you cook it. First, cut off the head, then make a cut down through the belly as far as the tail. Don't throw the entrails away – you can use them for baiting traps. Now peel off the skin, just like peeling a banana. Don't throw it away, either. Snakeskin and lizardskin are useful materials even before they're cured.

## Lizards
Treat large lizards just like snakes (they're not quite as easy to skin). Small lizards can be impaled on a stick through the head and roasted, without skinning and gutting them first. You'll know they're cooked when the skin starts to bubble and crack.

Reptile meat is very much like chicken, light in colour, moist and tender. Remember that in some parts of the world snake meat is regarded as a delicacy!

## Down by the waterside
Don't ignore the larger reptiles, like crocodiles, alligators and cayman. They, too, are edible, and the meat from just one large specimen will keep you going for a long time. Shoot them, if you can – in the back of the head or neck – but if you don't have a firearm available you could try trapping.

---

## Avoiding spiders and scorpions

**1** Check your bedding before you get into it.
**2** Check clothing, socks and shoes before you put them on.
**3** Avoid sleeping or leaving clothes near damp places; dampness appears to attract these creatures.
**4** If you feel an insect or spider crawling on you, remain still. Sudden movement may cause it to bite or sting.
**6** Never step in the shade of a bush without visually checking the spot.

## First Aid for scorpion stings

**1** Keep the patient quiet and send for medical aid.
**2** Place a tourniquet between the point of puncture and the heart.
**3** Cool the area for 10 or 12 inches around the puncture point with ice, if available.
**4** Remove the tourniquet after 10 minutes and keep the part chilled for at least two hours.

*Not a nice way to go – death by crocodile. They lie in wait in the shallows of lakes and slow-moving rivers, waiting for an animal (or you) to come down for a drink or a swim. The crocodile shown above contained the body of an Australian camper.*

These big reptiles are rather hard to skin. The best way is to heat them over a fire to loosen their armour and then skin them out in the normal way. The belly skin makes the most useful leather and, like all reptile skin, should be kept for use as bindings and straps. Skin from the rest of the animal is of little value.

## Small but nourishing

Also not to be overlooked (and easy to find) are smaller aquatic animals. Frogs, newts and salamanders (a type of aquatic lizard) will all provide protein, and so will keep you alive where all else fails.

Frogs are best hunted at night, when you can locate them by their croaking. Skin and gut them before cooking. All the meat is edible. You will find newts and salamanders are to be found wherever there are frogs. Look in the water and under rocks and rotten logs. As with frogs, skin and gut them before you cook them.

But do beware: certain frogs and salamanders have poisonous sacs in their skin.

Desert and tropical jungle abound with various types of dangerous invertebrate animal life such as ground-dwelling spiders, scorpions and centipedes, together with insects of almost every type. Drawn to man as a source of moisture or food, lice, mites and flies can be extremely unpleasant and can carry diseases such as scrub typhus and dysentery.

The stings of many scorpions and the bites of centipedes or spiders can be extremely painful, though seldom fatal. Some species of scorpions and

*Watch out for scorpions. They live under stones and in dark, warm, humid places in all warm countries. Your biggest danger is when walking around barefoot, putting boots back on, or finding them in your armpits when asleep.*

black widow or recluse spiders, however, can cause death. When you camp, check your clothes and shoes every morning.

Don't worry too much about tarantulas. These large, hairy spiders do have venom, but it rarely causes serious reactions in humans; you'll usually only get a slight swelling, numbness and itching.

**Remember: In many countries, including the UK, it is illegal to kill, injure or take reptiles.**

# Beware the unseen enemy

**Whatever the conditions in which you're trying to survive, you'll never see your worst enemies. They're the tiny botulism bacterium that thrives on rotting flesh; the poison molecule injected by a scorpion; the malaria passed on to you when a mosquito feeds on a tiny drop of your blood; the typhoid or cholera in the dirt on the feet of the fly that lands on your food; the bubonic plague carried by the fleas on the rat you ate yesterday.** This section of the Survival Course shows you how to combat threats to your health. Some are just irritating or painful; some of them are fatal.

People survived to a ripe old age long before there was a chemist's shop in every High Street, and most of that time they lived at least partly off the land. They had to deal with the same kinds of pests and dangers that you'll meet in the wild. And, over the years, they discovered ways of treating everyday complaints. Most of those ways will be available to you, too.

### Bites and stings

Insects are more likely to give you trouble than anything else you will meet in the wild, either from the poisons they produce themselves, or because of the diseases they carry and

*The tsetse fly makes a meal of human blood. In return, he passes on sleeping sickness a disease that produces fever, wasting away and sluggishness. The tsetse is common throughout Africa and vast numbers are afflicted by it.*

can transmit. Some people suffer more than others through being allergic to particular types of stings. If this is true for you, then carry the appropriate treatment kit on your body at all times. Not in your pack, because you may lose that or even have to abandon it, but actually on your body.

If you get a bite or a sting, don't scratch it; it may become infected as a result, and that infection may end up by killing you. In the tropics, especial-

*There are deadly spiders in all tropical parts of the world, and a single sharp bite can kill in seconds. Don't carelessly lift stones or logs; there may be one underneath.*

ly, the slightest scratch can lead to blood poisoning and even gangrene if it becomes infected.

Check all over your body at least once a day to see that no insect has attached itself to you. If you find a tick, which can transmit a variety of diseases, cover it with grease, tree sap or something similar, to cut off its air supply. Then it will release its hold and you can remove it. Don't squeeze its body. Wash your hands and the area of the bite immediately.

If you're stung by a bee, wasp or hornet, remove the stinger and the venom sac, if it's attached, by scraping gently with a fingernail or knife blade. Don't squeeze the venom sac; you'll be squeezing more of the poison into the wound. Wash the whole area straight away.

### Spiders, centipedes, scorpions and ants

These can all inflict a painful wound, and some may be fatal. In the case of spiders and scorpions, clean the wound completely, and try to suck the venom out by mouth or squeeze

the wound. Then treat it like any other open wound.

In the Middle East, watch out for the Camel Spider in particular. This creature, which can be as big across as a small plate, is a meat eater. Its bite is a local anaesthetic, so you don't feel it eating away around the wound site. In Australia, the Funnel-Web Spider is said to be the most dangerous; its bite is almost always fatal.

Like spiders, scorpions can be anything from half an inch to six or eight inches long. Some are fatal, some only produce a painful wound. If you take any article of clothing off, examine it carefully for spiders and scorpions before you put it back on again.

Treat centipede and ant bites like wasp stings. Well-chewed tobacco, placed on the wound after you've cleaned it, will sometimes help to ease the pain.

If you can find out what the local people use against stings and bites, then you can copy them, but you should be very careful.

## Open wounds

Normally, open wounds are dangerous because of tissue and fluid loss, and because of the shock to your system when they're inflicted.

Out in the middle of nowhere, with no proper medical kit, the greatest danger is from infection. Some infection is inevitable, but you can limit it and stop it spreading.

Clean the wound as soon as possible. That means:

**1** Remove or cut clothing away from the wound site
**2** Remove any obvious foreign bodies
**3** Clean the area around the wound carefully

*Disease is as big a killer in war as bullets. Millions upon millions died in this way in the jungles of Burma and China during World War II, and those diseases are just waiting out there for the next round. Personal hygiene is your number one priority.*

*Below and left: Not a welcome visitor, the tapeworm. You get these disgusting pests from eating undercooked meat. They attach themselves to your gut by the anchor arrangement shown left, whereupon they feast on your half-digested food. They grow to enormous size: the one below is about six metres long. Bits drop off the ends and migrate through your blood supply, lodging in inconvenient places such as your brain, where they start growing, with disastrous results.*

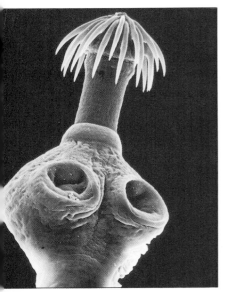

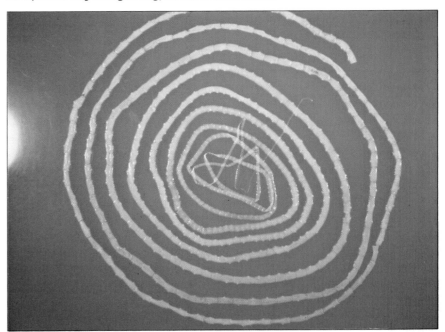

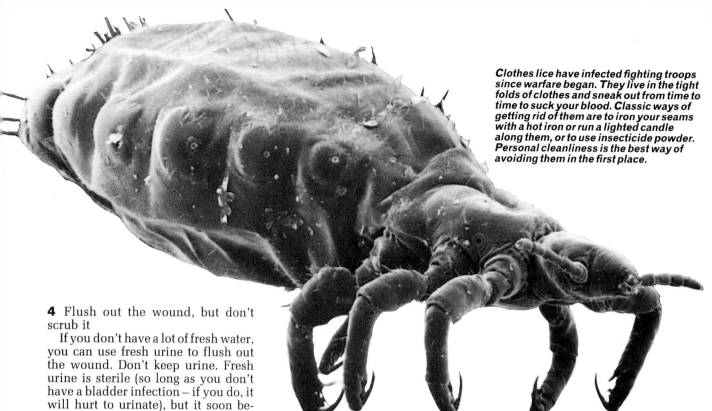

**4** Flush out the wound, but don't scrub it

If you don't have a lot of fresh water, you can use fresh urine to flush out the wound. Don't keep urine. Fresh urine is sterile (so long as you don't have a bladder infection – if you do, it will hurt to urinate), but it soon becomes contaminated.

Don't apply undiluted iodine or mercurochrome from your first-aid kit to a wound – it will only do more damage. You can use it to sterilise surrounding areas, as long as you're very careful.

Don't try and sew the wound up, no matter how much it's gaping open, though you can try to bind it. In survival conditions, it's bound to become infected anyway. Keep it open so that pus and infected material can drain away. To clean the wound, use a warm compress, directly on to the wound, for half an hour at a time, three or four times a day.

If the wound closes, open it with something sterile. A few moments in a flame will sterilise a knife blade or a piece of broken glass. Don't wipe it when you take it out of the flame. Let the pus drain out and remove any

accumulation of pus carefully, including any that has dried. Now dry the wound and dress it. And keep drinking as much water as you can. You must keep up this treatment until the wound starts to heal.

## Skin infections

Boils, fungal infections and rashes rarely develop into a serious problem on their own, but they can if you scratch them and introduce infection from your fingers.

Apply a warm compress to a boil, to bring it to a head, then open it up with a sterile knife or needles. Clean out the pus thoroughly. Keep the site dry with a dressing, and check it from time to time.

Keep the skin clean and dry around a fungal infection. Don't scratch it, and don't use iodine or disinfectant to

try and 'burn out' the infection – it doesn't work.

If you develop a heat rash, keep it clean and dry. If you have powder, then use it. Cold compresses may relieve the itching, but scratching won't.

## Stomach bugs and parasites

The best way to deal with parasites is to avoid them. Don't go around barefoot. Don't eat raw meat or fish if

*Below and left: These evil beasts live in your intestines and other sensitive tissues, drinking your bodily fluids and causing bilharzia, a widespread debilitating and deadly disease. You catch them by swimming in still tropical waters, where they burrow through your skin. The red threads in their stomachs are half-digested blood. Watch out for blood in your urine.*

you can possibly avoid it, especially liver, because that's where most parasites gather in the body. Don't eat raw vegetables that might be contaminated with faeces used as fertiliser.

If you do become infected with a parasite of some sort (watch out for worms or parts of them in your faeces, and for a feeling of general tiredness), you can try one of the following remedies:

**1** Drink two pints of salt water (do not repeat)

**2** Eat one or two cigarettes' worth of tobacco. Repeat after 24 hours, but no sooner, if necessary

**3** Drink two tablespoons of paraffin. Repeat after 24 hours, but no sooner, if necessary

**4** Eat hot peppers as a regular part of your diet

Bear in mind that these remedies can be uncomfortable and may damage your intestine.

Diarrhoea is generally caused by drinking contaminated water or eating contaminated food. Be careful of melons, vegetable marrows and other plants that contain huge amounts of moisture. They take up contamination along with the water. It doesn't bother the plant, but it will bother you.

Try one of these remedies:

**1** Take nothing but fluids for 24 hours

**2** Drink one cup of extra-strong tea every 2 hours until the diarrhoea

stops. It's the tannin in the tea that does the job. If you don't have tea, boil up the inner bark of a hardwood tree (one with broad leaves) for two hours or more. It will smell and taste quite awful.

**3** Make up a paste with clean water and ground-up chalk, charcoal or dried bone. Take two tablespoonsful every two hours. If you have oranges, lemons or other citrus fruits, add the white pith, or the squeezed-out flesh of an apple, to the mixture.

Drink lots of liquids after the attack has passed, to replace the body fluids you've lost in the meantime.

*Malaria kills more people than any other disease. Mosquitoes feed by sucking your blood, but at the same time they squirt anticoagulants into your bloodstream along with the malaria parasite. These creatures then take up residence in your blood cells, where they multiply and burst the cell walls. Moral: keep taking the tablets.*

## The Maggot Treatment

As recently as the First World War, maggots were an accepted way of dealing with infected wounds. Before you decide to use them as a treatment, however, there are a couple of factors you should consider:

**1** Maggots are the larvae of flies. To produce them, you have to let flies lay their eggs in the wound. Because flies carry all sorts of other infections around with them, you run the risk of complicating the situation further.

**2** Maggots will eat healthy tissue just as happily as infected tissue.

Even so, if you have a severe case of infection and no antibiotics, you should consider maggot treatment if the wound shows no signs of healing on its own. This is how you go about it:

**1** Expose the wound to flies for one day, then cover it up and check it regularly.

**2** When the maggots appear, keep the wound covered, but keep checking on its progress.

**3** When the maggots have eaten their way through the infected flesh, remove them. Increased pain and bright, fresh blood in the wound indicate that the maggots are into healthy flesh.

*Maggots feast on dead flesh. They say that wounds cleaned by maggots heal very well indeed.*

**4** Flush the wound several times with fresh urine.

**5** Check the wound every four hours for several days, to make sure that no maggots remain.

**6** Bandage the wound and treat it normally.

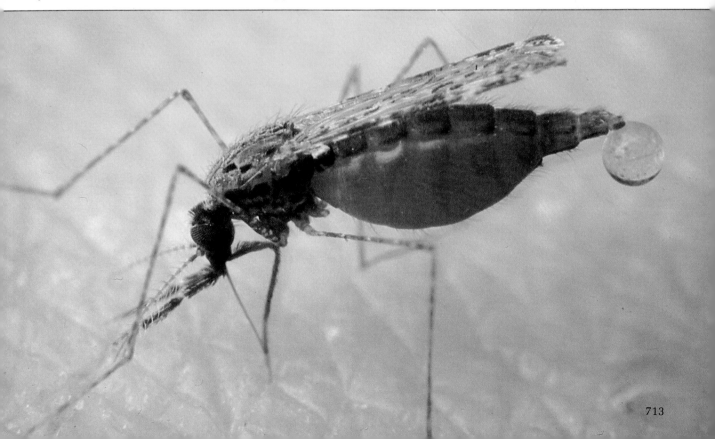

# Survival

# Herbal Healers

**The warm damp air holds the strong scent of the pine trees, but the beauty of the moment is lost to you — faced with the prospect of a cold spring night without a fire, you're busy chopping a piece of dead birch into the hearth piece of a fire bow.** The sweat of your labour does not go unnoticed. You're also providing a meal for several horseflies. Distracted for only a moment, you feel the razor edge of your knife slicing flesh instead of wood.

You've got a deep cut across your finger, but the muscle and bone, luckily, are undamaged. As the cut begins to fill with blood you wrap it in some torn material, take a long gulp of water from your canteen and, sitting up against a tree with your injured hand on your head, wait for the inevitable faint nausea to pass.

## From minor to major

Normally your injury would be hardly worth worrying about. But since you're sleeping rough, working hard, on a reduced diet and with poor washing and toilet facilities, your minor injury will prove fatal if neglected. Without any medical kit you will have to improvise, keeping the wound clean with pure water and

*Four of the most crucial factors in staying healthy are having enough food and water, adequate rest and keeping clean. On exercise you are unlikely to get sufficient sleep or, perhaps, food. In war you will definitely be short of all four, and a sound knowledge of nature's herbal healers will be an advantage.*

sterilised bandaging. (You won't be able to produce perfectly sterilised bandages, but boiling until dry is the next best thing.) Don't underestimate the difficulty of keeping the wound free from infection.

A basic knowledge of medicinal plants will be invaluable to help you tackle the problems of survival.

# Four handy remedies

## Herbal medicine

Unlike modern high-powered drugs, most herbal remedies are slow acting. They work by encouraging your body's natural healing processes. Because they are so mild, there is very little risk of an overdose. If you are allergic to any cure you use, you'll find out before any serious harm is done. The mildness of most herbal cures is especially useful if you are in a weakened physical state.

Simplicity and hygiene are the secrets of self-medication in survival conditions. No matter how wretched you may feel, keep your personal standards high. Wash regularly – especially after relieving yourself. You need to keep your energy up, so eat as regularly as you can. Wash all food before cooking it, and try to avoid raw food altogether. Drink pure water or your favourite herbal tea. These steps will help ensure your body is capable of fighting your illness or infection.

When using your herbal medicines don't over-complicate matters with weird concoctions. Try your medicines individually and note their effects. You may notice only a subtle change over a period of several days.

## Safe medicinal plants

Exactly the same rules apply for medicinal plants as for edible ones. First, only use a medicinal plant you have positively identified as medicinal. Second, be certain you are using the plant in the correct manner for the correct ailment.

The best way to learn about medicinal plants is to carry a suitable field guide with you when you are on exercise. Many edible plants are also medicinal, but not all medicinal plants are edible. Many of the modern proprietary drugs that have been derived from plants were obtained from deadly poisonous varieties – for example, digitalis from foxglove, and atropine from deadly nightshade. The third rule of survival herbalism is: Never use a poisonous plant for medication. It is better to stick to plants that are both edible *and* medicinal.

## Problem and cure

Because you can't foresee the terrain where you will be injured, make yourself familiar with plants from many different habitats. The following cures are from ten of the safest and commonest medicinal plants to be found in the temperate zone. Familiarise yourself with these before studying further.

**Controlling bleeding:** The green stem of the Horsetail (*Equisetum Arvense*), when boiled or soaked to produce a tea, will help stop bleeding. Wash out the cut with the tea.

**Upset stomach:** Dog Rose (*Rosa Canina*) petals and the hips are excellent for settling the stomach after eating something vile – a common problem on Army exercises.

**Antiseptic:** An infusion (tea) made of the Greater Plantain (*Plantago Major*) will help prevent infection in a wound. In an emergency you can chew the leaf and apply the result directly to the wound.

**Preventing digestive problems:** While bad guts at home may be no real problem, on operations they can literally be the death of you. Adding horseradish roots and leaves to your daily ration pack will help prevent problems.

# The herbal compress

**1** Open wounds are vulnerable to infection especially as your body's resistance will be low after a prolonged period in the field. A compress of an antiseptic plant like Greater Plaintain is made by pulping the plant with a stone.

## Bleeding

A plant with haemostatic properties will help stop bleeding. You probably won't have such plants readily to hand when you first find yourself in survival conditions, so prepare and store these herbs in your survival medicine chest. The dried and powdered root of Bistort *(Polygonum bistorta)* can be applied direct to external wounds.

Use an infusion of the green stem of Horsetail *(Equisetum arvense)* to wash the wound. It will help stop the bleeding.

## Antiseptic

To prevent wounds becoming infected they can be washed with an infusion made with these medicines:
**1** Greater plantain *(Plantago major)* leaves and stem. In an emergency, chew the leaf of this plant to a pulp and use it directly on the wound.
**2** Selfheal *(Prunella vulgaris)* flowering stems. This plant too can be chewed, for a quickly prepared pulp.
**3** Dried burdock *(Arctium lappa)* root, made into an infusion. This is ideal to prepare for long journeys. The

leaves can also be infused but are less potent.
**4** Birch *(Betula pendula)* leaves when infused make an all-purpose disinfectant.

## Digestive disorders

An excellent cure for diarrhoea is charcoal and a herbal tea. Remember to keep your fluid intake high when suffering from diarrhoea.
**1** Dandelion *(Taraxacum officinale)* leaves, washed and eaten raw, or cooked like spinach, make an excellent aid to digestion. Try to include some in your survival diet as a preventative.
**2** Dog rose *(Rose canina)* petals and/or hip are a very good stomach settler. Before eating any of the vitamin-C-rich hips, remove the hairy seeds inside them.
**3** Water mint (Mentha aquatica) leaves and stems can be used as an infusion. This plant is also useful to flavour survival stews. Don't eat large quantities.
**4** Horseradish *(Armoracia rusticana)* roots and leaves in your daily diet will aid digestion and help pre-

vent problems. The scrapings from the root make a strong flavouring for stews.
**5** Selfheal flowering stems, infused, ease upsets. You can also prepare the leaves like spinach and include them in your diet.

For severe digestive disorders such as dysentery, use an infusion of powdered bistort root.

**2** Mop up the juice of the plant with the remaining flesh and gather it into a ball. Make sure you wash the stone beforehand.

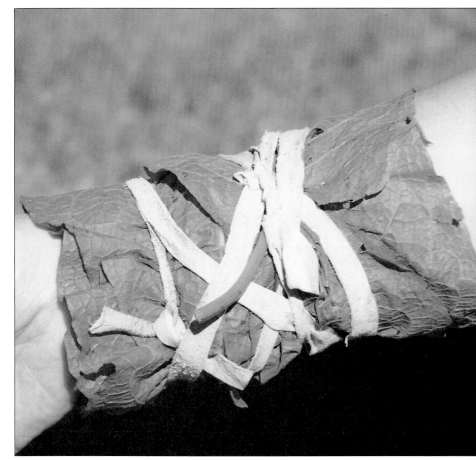

**3** Apply the herbal pulp firmly into and around the wound. Do not attempt to stitch up wounds of a superficial nature as you may stitch in the infection, and pressure caused by the infection and the stitching may lead to restricted blood flow to the area and then perhaps to gangrene. Cuts left open that heal in this way do leave nasty scars, but in the absence of sterile conditions and antibiotics this is the safer course.

**4** Keep the herbal pulp in place and maintain pressure on the wound with a wrapping of dock leaves held in place with strips of animal skin.

## Insect bites and stings

Insects are always an irritation for a survivor. Besides the diseases, such as malaria, that they carry, their bites and stings can quickly become painful festering sores if scratched. Use infusions of horsetail, burdock, plantain or birch to soothe the inflammations. You will probably find that after a couple of days of eating wild herbs insects will pay less attention to you, particularly if you include a small amount of plantain in your daily diet.

Deal with stings from stinging nettles by rubbing them with a fresh burdock leaf or a dock leaf.

### Bruises and headaches

You are certain to suffer some bruises and strains. To ease these, make compresses from bistort, horsetail or plantain.

Headaches are often encountered by survivors in the first few days of being stranded. Effective cures are soothing teas of mint or rose hips and/or petals.

### Toothache

Minor cuts, bruises and bites are relatively easy to deal with under primitive conditions. But when it comes to survival dentistry there is very little you can do. Rose tea can ease pain, but the best answer is to care properly for your teeth. This means regular visits to the dentist, and especially before going on extended operations. When stranded, clean your teeth with ash or alder *(Alrus glutinosa)* bark.

### Tips on preparing medicines

The secret of successful cures lies in how you choose and prepare your herbs. Try to collect only healthy plants, from areas of unpolluted ground. In wilderness areas, the best place to search for herbs are by water sources and where forest meets grassland. In escape and evasion situations, the edges of fields and along forestry rides are the places to search.

Having gathered your herbs, shake them clean of dust and insects. Most of the cures involve infusions, which basically means preparing the herb as a tea. Never boil your herb. Instead, allow it to brew in water just off the boil. This will retain all of the goodness in the plant.

Make paste for poultices by grinding up the herb between two rocks, with a little water. Apply this directly to the wound and wrap with cloth or large leaves.

You will have to judge the strength of your herbal cures by eye, as each plant has its own character, depending on the season or its location. If in doubt, always under-medicate.

THE CHARLIE 'G'
84-mm MAW

The 84-mm Medium Anti-Tank Weapon (MAW) is based on a Swedish-designed weapon known as the Carl Gustav. It is 112 cm long, weighs 16.35 kg and fires a High Explosive Anti-Tank (HEAT) projectile weighing 2.6 kg. The weapon is fitted with telescopic sights with a ×2

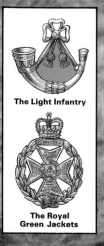

**The Light Infantry**

**The Royal Green Jackets**

*Firing the 84-mm from the prone position: you must keep your legs clear of the rear blast area. The shock on firing this weapon is truly impressive: two sets of ear defenders and a helmet are a must.*

**At the beginning of week 16 of your combat infantry training you're as well-qualified as you ever will be to face the three gruelling weeks of final battle camp.** This is the climax of your training, and your chance to show you've really learned everything you've been taught.

You travel to Wales in a civvy coach – all very comfortable, and it soon lulls you into a false sense of security. You arrive at a hutted camp nestling in the foothills of the Brecon Beacons. It's basic, but it's warm, and you make the best of it.

### The most exciting week

During this first week you live-fire, in field conditions, all the weapons that you've been introduced to in your previous 15 weeks at the depot. Field-firing week is probably the most exciting and rewarding seven days of your entire training.

As one test, you fire your SA80 in the 'battle pairs' competition. In this, you and your battle partner fight your way across a piece of very rugged countryside, taking on radio-controlled targets as they pop up at various distances from you. You finish by assaulting the enemy position you've been making for, throwing a live grenade before you charge in.

You also fire your SA80 on the individual Close Quarter Battle (CQB) range. Here, you advance slowly down a narrow, heavily wooded path. Suddenly targets appear from nowhere at ranges of between 10 and 20 metres. They disappear very fast, and you have to react to them instantly.

### Shooting night and day

On another range, the section fires both SA80 and LSW from a dug-in position, at night as well as by daylight. Targets first appear at 600 metres from the LSW to engage. As the enemy 'advances', targets appear at closer and closer ranges – until about 20 targets spring up 50 metres away to simulate the final enemy assault on your position.

The most exhilarating shoot of all is

## Aiming the optic sig

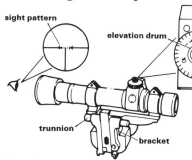

sight pattern

elevation drum

trunnion

bracket

The telescopic sight has a ×2 magnification and should always be used in preference to iron sights. The sight pattern consists of a vertical pointer which is used for stationary, withdrawing or advancing targets. On each side are the lead marks for aiming at crossing targets.

magnification and an iron sight. An Individual Weapon Sight (IWS), which has image intensification (II) capability, can be used for night firing. The weapon has a muzzle velocity of 310 metres per second and a range of up to 600 metres.

The 84-mm is the main section anti-tank weapon in the infantry. There is one in each section, a total of three in a platoon. It is designed to fill in gaps in Milan coverage and to provide short-range protection to Milan crews to overcome the weapon's minimum range problem. It is a shoulder-mounted recoilless weapon capable of disabling or destroying any known armoured fighting vehicle (AFV) provided you hit it in a vulnerable area. Although its primary role is anti-armour, the gun can be used against buildings in FIBUA and against gun emplacements and field defences. Although the sights are marked up to 600 m, the maximum effective range against a static target is 500 m and against a moving target 400 m. Because the gun is recoilless it provides a distinct flash and blast behind the gun. The danger area extends 30 metres rearwards with an angle of 800 mils to either flank of the line of fire.

The gun can be fired from the kneeling, standing or lying position. In all cases the No. 1 holds, aims and fires the weapon while the No. 2 opens the breech, removes the round from its container, loads the round, closes the breech, checks that the backblast area is clear and then, when the round has been fired, opens the breech and removes the empty case.

The No. 78 telescopic sight is the primary sighting system of the gun, and is very simple to use. The sight pattern consists of a vertical pointer, the tip of which is used to aim at stationary, head-on or withdrawing targets. On each side of the pointer are lead marks: lead

**1** On receiving the command 'tank action', No. 1 pushes the cocking rod forward, applies the safety catch and shouts 'load'.

**2** No. 2 repeats the command 'load', removes the rubber cap on the fuse assembly on the round, and opens the venturi.

**3** No. 2 loads the round into the weapon, keeping his thumb in the cut-out in the round so that it correctly locates.

**4** He then checks that the round is fully home, closes the venturi, taps back on the catch and shouts 'loaded'.

**5** No. 2 checks that the rear blast area is clear, and on the command 'stand by' from No. 1 faces forward and braces himself.

**6** Both firer and loader observe strike. No. 1 cocks the weapon and shouts 'load'. No. 2 opens the venturi and ejects the spent case.

**7** No. 2 then checks for fouling in the chamber, loads the next round and the firing cycle continues.

## Telescopic sight aim picture

Targets may be head-on or going away (1, right), or crossing – moving at any angle, showing some side (2, below).

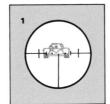

| Slow mover (8 km/h): first lead mark in centre of target | Battle mover (16 km/h): second lead mark in centre of target | Fast mover (32 km/h): third lead mark in centre of target |
|---|---|---|

## Sight alignment with iron sights

With a head-on or going-away target (1, right), dial in the range and aim at the centre of what you can see. Note that fairly

To achieve the correct aim on a crossing target (2, below), the pointer must be forward of the target.

| Slow mover (8 km/h): first lead mark in centre of target | Battle mover (16 km/h): second lead mark in centre of target | Fast mover (32 km/h): third lead mark in centre of target |
|---|---|---|

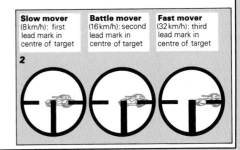

**deflection drum**

**range drum**

On the left of the bracket is the range drum. It has two sets of figures: white for anti-tank, graduated in 50-m units from 0 to 600 m, and green for use with anti-personnel ammo (which is not on issue, so ignore it).

the live-fire section attack. The LSW gunners stay put, sending out covering fire while you undertake a flanking attack.

It's a funny feeling, having the gun put down live-fire very close to you. As you assault the position, the LSW switches its fire in front of you. The instructors are watching the gunners closely all the time, but you still have to trust your mates to get it right, or you'll end up getting shot.

During live-firing week you also use both 66-mm and 84-mm anti-tank projectiles with practice warheads. It's exactly the same as firing a HEAT missile, except that it doesn't go bang the other end. One or two lucky guys in the platoon do fire a HEAT projectile – the whole platoon gets only one or two live rounds.

## Into the field

The second week of final battle camp is the platoon commander's final exercise. For this you move out of camp and live in the field for the whole week.

It's a tough exercise, and includes a three-day defence manoeuvre. For that you have to dig your own trench with your battle partner and live in it. You mount patrols at night from your defensive position, learn to put up wire defences and set trip flares. You get very little sleep.

The hardest part of final battle camp comes in the third week. You've now been out in the open for a week. You've had the minimum of sleep, and you're knackered. The week ends with a 25-mile approach march.

## The last battle

Your feet ache, you've probably got blisters, you're desperately tired, and you feel you're near the end of your tether. The march ends at an RV, where you leave your packs and prepare for a dawn attack against an enemy position.

The attack is incredible. The staff lay on the most amazingly realistic battle effects: burning tyres, trip flares, thunderflashes, parachute flares floating in the sky, and an enemy .30-cal machine-gun firing very noisy 'blank' rounds.

After the attack, you're taken down to the training camp. You're given a fantastic breakfast, a full fry-up. Then you take a blessed, beautiful hot shower. You clean your rifle, and then you collapse, utterly exhausted, into the coach, to sleep most of the four-hour journey back to the depot. You wake up only when the bus is entering the gates.

# Firing position

The weapon is usually fired as a two-man team – No. 1, who aims and fires the weapon, and No. 2, who loads – but it can if necessary be fired by one man.

*For moving targets, the kneeling position is best unless you're in a trench: prone is no good, and the standing position leaves you exposed.*

*A TPTP round (training practice tracer projectile) strikes low. You must boresight the weapon correctly to the telescopic and iron sights.*

*There are three types of ammunition currently available: TPTP (shown here), high explosive anti-tank (HEAT), and drill.*

*Ammo is issued in these plastic containers with the fuse protected by a rubber cap. The 84-mm must strike the target cleanly.*

one is a small square, lead two a short vertical line and lead three a long vertical line. These are used to aim at crossing targets. The horizontal lines are to assist in maintaining elevation when aiming. Sighting procedure is to estimate the range to the target to the nearest 50m and set it on the range drum.

A MAW team must learn how best to kill a tank. Clearly you must choose a concealed position so that you can engage a tank at close range. If a tank sees you from over 600 metres away he can engage you and there is nothing you can do to retaliate. So cover from view is most important, and this means hiding your backblast. The only way of doing this is to site your firing position in defilade so that your arc of fire is at right angles to the line of approach of enemy tanks. Then, at the moment of firing, the backblast is hidden from the other enemy tanks.

Secondly, you must aim at the most vulnerable parts of a tank. This means a side-on attack against the crew and troop-carrying areas of the vehicle or against the engine compartment. You can also achieve what is termed a 'mobility' kill by damaging the tracks or wheels of the vehicle so that it is unable to move.

If you are fighting in a built-up area you should try to avoid firing from confined spaces such as narrow streets and from the inside of buildings except in extreme emergency, because of the likely damage to your hearing and danger from backblast debris. If you are forced to fire from within a room, you should open all the doors and windows to reduce the effects of overpressure. Garden walls and demolished buildings provide adequate cover for most circumstances. Firing parallel to a wall should help to conceal the backblast.

The 84-mm MAW is particularly suitable for tank ambush and tank hunting. It is a short-range weapon and relatively light, so it can be carried on a night patrol to attack enemy tanks in a night leaguer. Such an attack is likely to be an 'in and out' affair that depends on surprise for success. Once you have fired you will have compromised your position, and will need to use the cover of darkness to slip away to cover your withdrawal.

Training on the 84-mm will take place between weeks 7 and 15 of your basic training. You will also fire it live during your Final Battle Camp in weeks 15-18. Because of the expense of firing an 84-mm HEAT round during your training, you will use a 6.5-mm sub-calibre device designed to have the same trajectory and range as the 84-mm round, but which is much cheaper.

The only effects missing are those of the noise and backblast. In order to train the MAW team to cope with the backblast and noise created by the HEAT round, an 84-mm practice round is also issued. This produces exactly the same effect, except that it does not have a high explosive warhead and does not therefore explode upon impact with the target. You will fire with the sub-calibre device up to 500 metres at the stationary and moving targets and then fire one 84-mm practice round on your final battle camp. Normally one 84-mm HEAT round is issued per platoon, which one lucky recruit will fire in order to demonstrate its effect.

# Combat Report
## Rhodesia:
## Zambian Border Action

**An officer serving with the Rhodesian African Rifles during the Rhodesian war describes an action near the border with Zambia in 1975.**

Early one morning, near the Mozambique border, I received an urgent message that there had been a new, unexpected incursion of about 85 guerrillas from Zambia. We were to leave for a small town called Kario, about 300 miles to the north. We packed hastily and, following a tiring journey, eventually arrived at Kario where I was briefed and given orders. The guerrillas had ambushed a 'tsetse fly control' vehicle and wounded one man. Local security forces had followed the enemy and, in a contact, had captured a wounded terrorist, plus some equipment.

We now deployed in the rain. By this time a detachment from the Rhodesian Light Infantry had joined us. There was soon another contact, with two enemy killed and one wounded. One of my subalterns, Lieutenant Ed, leading a 16-man patrol, quickly got on the trail.

### All hell broke loose

As they approached some rising ground, Ed's sergeant, a tough Ndebele, indicated enemy ahead, and he and three other men moved off to the left to start an encircling movement. At that moment, all hell broke loose as 24 guerrillas on the ridge ahead opened fire. They had obviously been waiting, but thanks to the sergeant they opened fire a bit too early.

Ed led his men in a charge, straight at the enemy position. This action clearly surprised them as their shots became high and erratic. When the RAR reached the crest, the enemy broke and fled. Three of them tried to break back around the side of the ridge, but ran straight into the sergeant and his men and were shot dead. Apparently one of these three was the Sectorial Political Commissar.

The ridge had been some sort of assembly point. There was a mass of enemy equipment on it, plus various weapons and a number of landmines. There was also a lot of blood, indicating that many guerrillas had been wounded. All in all, this was a successful action, thanks to Ed's brave leadership.

### The Claymores were spectacular!

Now we had to move base camp as the enemy were withdrawing. The heavy rain and low cloud caused problems when the helicopters withdrew the obervation posts from the mountains. It also made travel somewhat difficult, quite apart from the normal risks of ambush or landmines.

We hadn't been long at our new base when I heard some strange stuff coming over the radio: English-speaking voices, giving details of a contact, but not giving any familiar call-signs! It turned out to be the Special Air Service. They had anticipated that some of the guerrillas would return to a known enemy base just inside Mozambique, near the north-east corner of Rhodesia. They had parachuted in and laid an ambush using Claymores along the track leading to this base. The results were spectacular. I heard one voice on the radio say, "There are bodies all over the place, lots of them up in the trees!". The death toll was 18.

Then a civilian was arrested and admitted to assisting the enemy. He agreed to lead us to a terrorist camp containing 25 guerrillas. I decided to lead this attack, and the rest of the evening was spent planning. We set off in the pre-dawn darkness to a drop-off point a few miles from the enemy camp. En route I received a message from another platoon who were joining us for this operation. During the night they had been attacked by an unknown number of guerrillas, who used small-arms fire and mortars. However, they easily beat off the assault and their opponents fled into the darkness, leaving behind a Russian SKS automatic rifle plus magazines and ammunition.

When we met the platoon, I briefly examined the captured weapon. Then the assault force, now a company strong, moved on, led by the informer. As we drew nearer to the camp I sent one platoon to carry out a wide flanking movement to get behind the enemy. I expected to bump into a sentry and so, obviously, did our informer, as he became very nervous.

### The birds had flown

The trees we had been moving through suddenly thinned out. We had arrived at the camp. We were in extended order, and I gave the hand signal to attack. We charged, but – anti-climax – the birds had flown. Very disappointing, but as one of my young officers said, "You can't win 'em all!" All we found were some well-concealed resting places and a Chinese communist badge.

Shortly after this we returned to our base near Bulawayo for rest from operations. The operation continued with other troops, and by the time we left the opposition had lost 24, plus two known wounded and one captured. Not bad, considering only one of our men was slightly wounded.

**The Rhodesian army was made up of a number of nationalities with a taste for choosing their own weapons. From left to right: RPK Soviet LMG, FN FAL, RPD, RPG rocket launcher (on ground) and AKM assault rifle, held by the only Rhodesian present.**

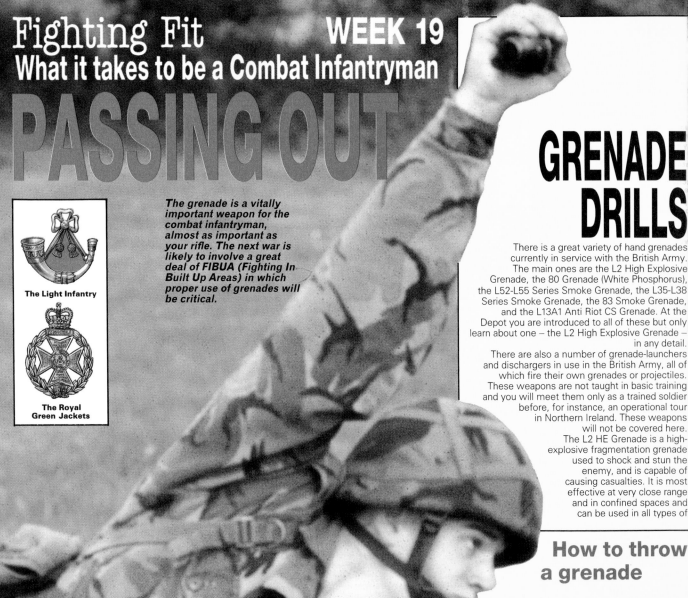

# Fighting Fit
## What it takes to be a Combat Infantryman

**WEEK 19**

# PASSING OUT

**The Light Infantry**

**The Royal Green Jackets**

*The grenade is a vitally important weapon for the combat infantryman, almost as important as your rifle. The next war is likely to involve a great deal of FIBUA (Fighting In Built Up Areas) in which proper use of grenades will be critical.*

# GRENADE DRILLS

There is a great variety of hand grenades currently in service with the British Army. The main ones are the L2 High Explosive Grenade, the 80 Grenade (White Phosphorus), the L52-L55 Series Smoke Grenade, the L35-L38 Series Smoke Grenade, the 83 Smoke Grenade, and the L13A1 Anti Riot CS Grenade. At the Depot you are introduced to all of these but only learn about one – the L2 High Explosive Grenade – in any detail.

There are also a number of grenade-launchers and dischargers in use in the British Army, all of which fire their own grenades or projectiles. These weapons are not taught in basic training and you will meet them only as a trained soldier before, for instance, an operational tour in Northern Ireland. These weapons will not be covered here.

The L2 HE Grenade is a high-explosive fragmentation grenade used to shock and stun the enemy, and is capable of causing casualties. It is most effective at very close range and in confined spaces and can be used in all types of

## How to throw a grenade

The following sequence shows you how to throw an L2 anti-personnel grenade. Remember to keep a firm grip on the grenade so that the lever does not move out of the web of your hand before throwing.

**1** On a grenade range, you obtain your grenade and fuse in one bay before going round the corner to the actual throwing bay.
**2** Inspect for damage, fit the grenade onto its fuse mechanism, and screw it up tight.
**3** On the command 'Change!' you move from the primary bay into the throwing bay.
**4** Face the safety supervisor. He will ask you whether you are right- or left-handed and will check that you aren't going to hit the back wall when you swing. On the command 'Prepare to throw!', take the grenade out of your pouch, place it firmly in your right (or left) hand with the fly-off lever in the web of your hand, and put your index finger through the pin, holding the grenade at waist level.
**5** On the command 'Throw!' pull the pin, visually check that it is out, and look at the target. Keeping your left shoulder (if you are right-handed) lined up on the target, swing your body and right arm backwards and allow your left arm to come up naturally.
**6** Swing upwards and release the grenade as your arm reaches its highest point. Remember to shout 'Grenade!' as you do so. Watch where the grenade lands. On the command 'Down!', and not before, take cover behind the wall.

---

*You've survived drill sergeants, muscle-busters and even final battle camp – now it's your final week of combat infantry training, and at the end of it you'll be on the passing-out parade, ready to join your unit.* Before then, there's still plenty to get done.

Not everyone's so lucky. If you get injured, or the instructors feel you didn't pull your weight at final battle camp, you have to be 'retrained'. That's the nice word the depot has for what the recruits call 'backsquadding', and it means joining the next platoon in the training cycle at week 13 and having another go at final battle camp.

Some people do need the extra time and, like it or not, the system gets it right more often than not. So if you are nominated for retraining, stick with it. It seems like a blow at the time, but the extra six weeks go extra fast – and, before you know it, you're passing out with the next platoon and you've made a whole lot of new mates into the bargain.

### At the double

But, if you make it through final battle camp without trouble, you return to the depot for one last hectic week. In those final few days you have to practise for the passing-out parade. You have to prepare your uniform and equipment for the parade, and you have to know your part perfectly for the PT display that's scheduled to follow it.

You also hear which battalion in the regiment it is that you are being posted

722

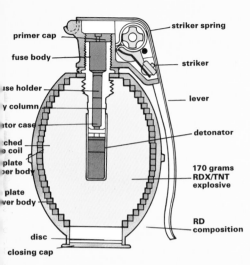

primer cap
fuse body
use holder
y column
ator case
tched
e coil
plate
er body
plate
ver body
disc
closing cap

striker spring
striker
lever
detonator
170 grams
RDX/TNT
explosive
RD
composition

**GRENADE**

GREN
A PERS L2A2

216    CY 10-80
172 APX 80

**FUSE**

close-quarter battle such as trench or bunker clearing, fighting in built-up areas or wood clearing. The distance at which casualties can be caused depends upon the hardness of the ground, and may be as much as 190 metres from the point of burst. Consequently, even in war, it is most important that you lie down behind cover when a grenade is thrown by a member of your own section.

Before you throw the grenade you remove the pin; when you throw the grenade you release the lever, thus allowing the striker to strike and fire the percussion cap, which ignites delay pellets. These burn for four or five seconds, then set off the detonator, which in turn detonates the HE filling. The explosion rips open the tinplate body of the grenade and, at the same time, breaks up the compressed steel wire coil, which is notched at intervals to assist fragmentation.

The grenade consists of a tin plate body and an L2 fuse assembly, which is issued separately from the grenade. Inside the body of the grenade is an HE filling surrounded by a compressed steel wire coil. At the top is a fuse holder, which receives the fuse assembly. It is only when the two are

put together that a lethal weapon exists. The fuse assembly contains a striker mechanism, which works on the mousetrap principle and is already cocked. The striker is held back against its spring by a fly-off lever secured to the fuse body by a split safety pin and ring.

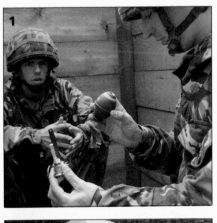

1

2

3

4

5

6

# Fighting Fit

to. You're given a choice and, usually, you get it. One battalion may be in the mechanised role in Germany, one may be on operations in Northern Ireland and another may be stationed in Gibraltar, Belize, Cyprus or Singapore.

### Sprucing up

The day of the passing-out parade dawns. You get up early to put the finishing touches to your kit. The Army has taught you to take a pride in your appearance and, even more important, your mum and dad and family and girlfriend are coming all the way from home to watch the parade.

### On the square

The parade lasts about 45 minutes. The inspecting officer arrives, a high-ranking general or the Lord Lieutenant of the county or the Mayor of the city. He inspects the platoon while the band plays. Then you march past. It's great with the music playing, the crowd watching – you feel it's been worth all the effort for this moment.

### Prizegiving

You advance in review order, and present arms. Then the prizes are presented – best recruit, best rifle shot, best LSW shot, best battle pair, best mapreading, best at signals (radio), most improved recruit, best at drill and a cup for the best section. Next comes the Speech by the Inspecting Officer; he usually gives you some good advice. Then you march past for the final time. There's a quick change into PT kit while the regimental free-fall parachute team drops in, then you take part in a demonstration of unarmed combat.

Finally, the platoon commander asks permission to dismiss the parade. He turns around and gives the order: 'To your battalions, fall out.' You turn

*Coloured smoke grenades such as the L55 are used as signals; usually to show other friendly forces where you are.*

and, with your mates of 19 weeks' hard training, rush across the square shouting at the top of your voice. You've made it. You've succeeded where a third of the platoon has fallen by the wayside. You're one of the élite – you're a trained combat infantryman in the most professional army in the world. You feel like you could take on anybody – and win!

---

When you are fighting in close country or in a built-up area, it is sometimes necessary to lob a grenade through a window or a door or into some small target area. In this sort of situation you should select a throwing position that will also protect you from the blast quite close to the target. You must then plan a route to the selected throwing position and move to it either undetected or using normal fire-and-manoeuvre techniques. The best method is then to lob the grenade underarm through the aperture.

The technique for throwing smoke grenades is exactly the same, but remember you are trying to create a smoke screen *between* yourself and the enemy, so you should aim to land the grenade on your side of the enemy

position. Also, you should take wind effects into account. In the case of the 80 grenade smoke is instantaneous but with the L52-55, L35-38 and 83 grenade it takes a few seconds to build up into an effective smokescreen. Remember, the L52-55 and L35-38 grenades are primarily designed as signal grenades to mark friendly forces to friendly aircraft or to indicate a position to an incoming helicopter, or for a similar signalling purpose.

The purpose of the Anti-Riot L16A1 grenade is obvious.

During basic training, the L2 grenade is thrown by every recruit on a grenade range designed to avoid accidents. There is a throwing bay and a priming bay, and a means of escape

from the throwing bay in more than one direction in case anyone drops a grenade by accident.

The thrower enters the priming bay, where the L25 fuse assembly is inserted into the L2 under supervision. He then walks into the throwing bay, where a second NCO supervises the business of throwing. The range is run by the officer-in-charge overlooking both bays from an armoured tower.

Throwing your first grenade is a frightening but exciting experience. It takes calm nerves and concentration. It's important you get it right, because the ability to throw a grenade accurately in combat may one day ensure that you survive and that you kill the enemy.

---

# THE 80 GRENADE

The 80 grenade, like the HE grenade, is issued in two parts. It is a very dangerous piece of kit, so only screw the fuse assembly to the body just prior to going on an operation. Unlike other smoke grenades, the 80 produces instant smoke. It has a considerable bursting radius and a wide range of offensive uses, especially in FIBUA and bunker-busting.

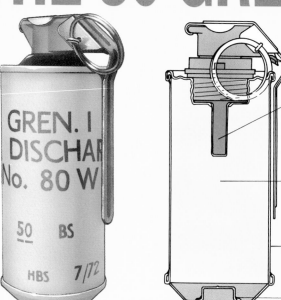

GREN. I
DISCHAR
No. 80 W
50    BS
HBS    7/72

**striker mechanism**

**tinned brass detonator tube**

**approx 330 grams of white phosphorus**
White phosphorus burns through whatever it gets onto, and gives off phosphorus pentoxide gas, which is highly toxic. Phosphorus produces horrific burns: wounds should be kept drenched with water. If possible, submerge the affected area completely.

**tinned plate body**

This shaped piece at the base of the grenade enables you to tell the difference between the white phosphorus 80 grenade and the harmless signal grenades.

**22-in rim-fire rifle cap**

**cap chamber**

**fuse, grenade Mk 1**

**aluminium detonator tube**

**ASA composition 5.4 grains**

**CE composition 3.9 grains**